Garrie L. Tufford

The Origin of Cultivated Plants

FRANZ SCHWANITZ

The Origin of
Cultivated Plants

HARVARD UNIVERSITY PRESS
CAMBRIDGE, MASSACHUSETTS · 1967

Second printing

CONTENTS

Natural and Artificial Selection. "Primary" and "Secondary"
Cultivated Plants. The Native Habitats of Cultivated Plants. On
the "Degeneration" of Cultivated Plants.

Origin and Age of Our Most Important Cultivated Plants. The
Stages of Development of Plant Breeding. Aims and Accomplishments of Plant Breeding.

The Origin of Cultivated Plants

CHAPTER 1

From Wild Plant to Cultivated Form

THE DERIVATION OF CULTIVATED PLANTS FROM WILD VARIETIES

The lives of all of us depend upon the existence of cultivated plants. Their importance to the development of the human race can be clearly seen by the fact that a hunter or forager needs roughly 20 square kilometers to sustain him, whereas the same area under cultivation can support 6000 people. If men were still dependent on hunting and foraging as the only sources of food, the earth could not support more than 30 million people. Cultivated plants alone make it possible for 2.5 billion to populate the globe today. Thanks to the high yield of these plants, our existence is not wholly taken up with the need to provide ourselves with food. Through the cultivation of plants, man has been freed from the compulsion of a nomadic existence and has settled down. Cultivated plants have facilitated the division of labor and have given man a certain amount of leisure, both of which are important prerequisites for the growth of science and technology. Thus cultivated plants have become the foundation of present-day civilization. Moreover, their best products are among the most valuable goods of human civilization—delicious vegetables, high-quality fruit, noble wines. And the ornamental plants of our gardens, with their perfect forms, marvelous colors, and various fragrances, satisfy our aesthetic sense and form a part of our culture that we might well place on an equal plane with the arts.

As cultivated plants are a prerequisite and an integral part of every advanced civilization, so are they the creation of man, and, considering the important role that their development has played in our cultural evolution, we might well say that their creation has been one of the greatest achievements of the human mind.

Cultivated plants have by no means always existed in their present forms and capacities, just waiting to be discovered, found useful, and grown by man. Rather, they derive from wild species, in which the qualities that are so valuable to us in cultivated plants are usually developed very imperfectly. Most of these original wild forms are known to us today. A cultivated form can easily be traced back to a certain wild species if the plant was grown and transformed into an actual cultigen within historic times. This is the case, for instance, with our native berries—gooseberry, currant, raspberry, and wild strawberry—which were not planted in our gardens before the late Middle Ages. Tracing is more difficult if this transformation occurred very early, say in early historic or even prehistoric times. Such cultivated plants must be traced back to their original wild forms by finding out the relationships among various wild species, that is, by judging the greater or lesser similarities that exist between them. With the help of this method, which was developed through systematics and by which that branch of science made it possible to clarify to a large extent the relationships of animals and of plants, De Candolle, in his classic work *Origine des plantes cultivées,* was able to answer satisfactorily, in the second half of the last century, the question of the origin of a number of our most important cultivated plants.

The following example will illustrate how the descent of a cultivated plant from a particular wild species can be shown to be probable on the basis of extensive similarity in the form of the plants. Emmer (*Triticum dicoccum*) is one of the oldest cultivated plants of the Old World. The original wild form was unknown for a long time. It was not until the middle of the nineteenth century, first in Syria, then in Palestine, and eventually in various places in the Middle East, in particular Persia, that a wild species of grass was discovered that evidently belonged to the wheat genus *Triticum*. Of all species of wheat, this one was by far the most similar to emmer. This species and emmer corresponded in all essential characters, and the deviations were only of the kind that are usually found between cultivated and wild forms. In this case, the wild form was generally smaller and more delicate than the more robust cultivated form. The spikelets were considerably more slender, and the fruitlets smaller and narrower. Moreover, the spikelets of the wild grass were very hairy, and those of emmer were not. Finally, the spike of the wild form divided spontaneously into individual spikelets when ripe, while that of emmer had a tough shank. From the close similarity of the two forms in all systematically important characters, with deviations only in such characters as usually differentiate wild plants and cultivated forms, the conclusion could be drawn that the newly discovered species of grass, named *Triticum dicoccoides*, was the wild progenitor of emmer (Fig. 1).

The knowledge gained by these methods about the wild progenitors of our cultivated plants has since been supplemented and increasingly filled in by research on prehistoric times.

Charles Darwin, in his famous works *On the Origin of Species* and *The Variation of Animals and Plants under Domestication*, took up the problem of the origin of our cultivated forms. In contrast with De Candolle, he was less concerned with the question of habitat and tracing cultivated plants from particular wild varieties, seeking above all to

Fig. 1. (*Left*) Ears of wild emmer, *Triticum dicoccoides,* and (*right*) of emmer, *T. dicoccum.* The ear of the wild form is smaller in virtually all parts and shatters into individual spikelets when ripe.

discover the natural laws that make possible the trans-formation of wild species into cultivated forms. As the motivating forces of this process he recognized, first, the tendency of organisms to "variate," that is, to produce new inheritable forms over and over again, and, second, the "artificial" selection of suitable variants by man.

Through the work of De Candolle and Darwin, the main lines of research in the study of cultivated plants were set up: inquiry into the origin and habitats of cultivated plants and inquiry into the motivating forces that led to the evolution of plant forms so significant to mankind.

The discovery of the laws of heredity by Carl Correns, Hugo De Vries, and Erich von Tschermak around the turn of the century, and the subsequent rapid development of genetics, provided new and valuable possibilities for research on cultivated plants. By crossbreeding cultivated forms with closely related wild species and by genetic and cytogenetic analysis of the offspring of these crosses, it became possible, by systematic study, to verify the derivation of cultivated plants from certain wild forms. Furthermore, it could now be shown how, in a given case, a wild form had been trans-formed into a cultivated plant by means of various changes in its genetic constitution.

Outstanding results in this new field were obtained by the Russian botanist Vavilov and his students. Vavilov made an inventory of the diverse forms of our most important cultivated plants and their distribution over the various parts of the earth by means of a comprehensive collection of plant material gathered from all over the world. In this way, he succeeded in establishing the native habitats of most of our cultivated plants. In Germany, the botanist Elisabeth Schiemann, more than anyone else, extended and deepened our understanding of this field by numerous experimental studies and by collecting our knowledge of the origin of cultivated plants into two comprehensive works.

Through the studies of many botanists doing various kinds of research, we have come to know the original wild forms of a great many cultivated plants. Thus we are in a position to establish which characters undergo changes during the evolution of plants from wild to cultivated forms, and what these changes are.

GATHERED PLANTS AS THE FIRST FORMS
OF CULTIVATED PLANTS

Before looking further into the differences between wild and cultivated plants, we must touch on the question of how man began intentionally to plant certain wild species and to create conditions giving rise to the characteristics of cultivated plants and for the gradual transformation of wild forms into actual cultivated plants.

The first cultivated plants that man possessed doubtless came from "gathered plants,"* that is, from plants that—as wild forms—man already esteemed for their valuable properties. The gathering of wild plants is not restricted to prehistoric times, to the early days of human history, or to the primitive civilizations of our era. In supplying modern man with food and raw materials, gathered plants play a role that should not be underrated. The harvesting of wild plants, or parts of them, has not been abandoned even in countries having highly developed agriculture. Thus every year in Germany large quantities of wild berries—raspberries, blackberries, and especially blueberries and lingonberries—are brought to market, and still more are gathered

*This is a literal translation of "Sammelpflanzen." Even though not currently used in English, it is accurate and appropriate, since the term "food gatherers" is now widely employed and understood.

by people for their own consumption. With the exception of the field mushroom, which is grown in a special cultivated form, the Japanese *shiitake,* and a few other species, all the mushrooms we eat are collected in woods, meadows, and pastures. The hazelnuts of German hedgerows are a special favorite of the young people, and on the Bergstrasse the chestnuts, which have been growing wild there since Roman times, are eagerly picked up when they are ripe by the whole populace. In many places the berries of the common European elder, *Sambucus nigra,* the European red elder, *S. racemosa,* the wild sloe plums, and rose hips are also highly esteemed wild fruits. And finally, the majority of the medicinal herbs in our drugstores and pharmacies come, even today, from wild plants.

The same holds true for the collecting of parts or products of wild plants in other countries having a highly developed agriculture. Every year in the spring in the United States the rising sap of the sugar maple, *Acer saccharum,* is collected by tapping the trunks and is then boiled down into the popular maple syrup. The grain of the "wild" or "Indian" rice, *Zizania aquatica,* a large kind of grass growing along the shores of the lakes and rivers of North America, was one of the most important foodstuffs of the North American Indians, and is still considered a special delicacy in North America. In the southwestern United States and in Mexico various wild species of cactus are gathered plants. The fleshy leaves of some species are used for cattle feed and in the preparation of vegetable dishes and sweets. The fruits are often eaten as delicacies; thus one species is called the prickly pear. And the notorious narcotic mescal is obtained from the buttons of peyote, a small cactus with the technical name *Lophophora williamsii* var. *lewinii.*

The large varieties of sea algae that we know under the

collective term "seaweed" have also long been gathered
plants. Since ancient times they have served as food for the
inhabitants of coastal regions. Even now, *Laminaria digitata*,
a large brown alga, is eaten in quantities in the Far East; it
also grows in Heligoland. It is roasted, coated with sugar,
and made into cakes. Because of its high mannitol content,
it is used as a sweetener. And on the North Sea coast
various species of algae were still being consumed during
the past century. The famous edible birds' nests of Far
Eastern cuisine consist mostly of parts of red algae. From
these algae, along the coasts of the Indian Ocean and the
China Sea, is prepared the well-known agar, which has been
a popular food in the Far East since ancient times. This
product has become indispensable in modern bacteriology
and microbiology for the preparation of culture media. The
Irish moss of our pharmacies consists of the dried parts of
several species of red algae, particularly *Chondrus crispus*
and *Gigartina mamillosa.* Bougies, whose swelling capacity
is used for dilating wound canals and similar tubular pas-
sages, are made from the dried stems of the alga *Laminaria
hypoborea*. In coastal regions where there is a shortage of
fodder, seaweed has always been used for feeding cattle.
Linnaeus wrote that bladder wrack, *Fucus vesiculosus,* was
called *Schweinetang* [pigweed] in Gotland because, mixed
with other fodder, it was used for feeding pigs; it is still
used in Scotland as winter fodder for sheep and cattle.
This kind of use is regaining importance for the agriculture
of coastal areas, for it has been found that these large
marine algae not only have a high vitamin content, but
also contain a large number of vital trace elements. Marine
algae were also used in early times as raw material in the
chemical industry. Since the middle of the eighteenth
century soda and potash have been produced from the ash
of these plants, and in the second half of the nineteenth

century they were the most important source of iodine and bromine. Because of the discovery of better and cheaper raw materials for the production of these substances, the marine algae have lost their former importance for the production of inorganic chemicals. They have instead become valuable, in recent years, as a source of raw material for obtaining economically important organic chemicals. Some species of algae found in Europe, especially on the Atlantic coasts of Ireland, Scotland, and Norway, contain, in addition to valuable gelatinous substances, up to 40 percent dry weight of alginic acid. From this are obtained algins, which are used in the textile industry for producing sizing materials, in surgery as a remedy, in dentistry as a base for dental-impression materials, in the prevention of boiler scale, as an additive to cosmetic products, and as a food thickener and in food coloring. Thus an old group of gathered plants has gained new economic importance. If on the coasts of Japan and America care is taken in the conservation and propagation of valuable species of algae, marking the first step toward cultivation of these plants, this may well be the beginning of cultivation of the large marine algae.

Even today wild plants may be grown by man for the first time and, circumstances permitting, be converted into new cultivated plants. This is well demonstrated by the sea buckthorn, *Hippophaë rhamnoides.* This shrub grows in sandy soil on the sea coast and in the gravelly sand on the banks of rivers. Its bright red-orange fruits contain up to 1200 mg percent of vitamin C, as well as carotene, or pro-vitamin A. The high biological value of the fruit of the sea buckthorn is responsible for the interest that cultivators have taken in trying to transform this wild plant into a true cultivated plant.

Gathering wild plants takes quite a lot of time, and it is

no longer worth while in an intensive economy. As a general trend, therefore, the gathering of wild plants is decreasing more and more with the increase of agricultural progress. In the course of time, therefore, a large part of the plants once gathered have disappeared from the group of plants used by man. Manna grass, *Glyceria fluitans,* which grows on the shores of inland waters, was used in the early days of the nineteenth century in the preparation of manna croup. With the exception of some botanists, no one knows today that this wild grass once had a role in human nutrition. The fruit of the water chestnut, *Trapa natans,* a floating plant now found only in a few places in Germany, was once an important food in central Europe. Water chestnuts are still consumed in Italy, southern Russia, India, and the Far East.

Acorns are an ancient gathered fruit; they have not been used for human consumption for centuries, but they were still used in the Middle Ages as a kind of fruit for bread-making, and for a much longer time have been used to eke out bread-flour supplies, at least in times of famine. The two world wars and the years following them reminded us vividly that beechnuts can make a valuable contribution to our sustenance.

In such times of need, we remember the almost forgotten edible wild plants and try to fill the gaps in our provisions with "the food of the forest." Once the food supply gets back to normal, modern civilized man quickly returns to cultivated plants as his only source of vegetable food. The great importance of wild plants in the support of man is reflected in normal times—except for mushrooms and certain wild berries—only by scanty remnants and traces. Some of these are the "soup of nine herbs" prepared in some parts of Germany at Eastertime from the leaves of yarrow, dandelion, goutweed, stinging nettle, sorrel, adderwort, brooklime, prickmadam or stonecrop, and wood sorrel, or the "wild salads" of corn salad or lamb's lettuce, dandelion, or watercress, all of which serve to remind us of the great importance wild plants have had in man's nutrition.

The fates of plants that at one time were gathered by man for use vary greatly. A large number of them have remained wild plants, used only in times of need. There are some plants, as, for instance, the beach grasses *Elymus arenarius* and *Ammophila arenaria,* the sand sedge, *Carex arenaria,* and the ditch reed, *Phragmites communis,* whose edibility is no longer remembered, while closely related species, such as *Elymus giganteus,* are still eagerly gathered by the Mongols.

Other gathered plants that seem more valuable to man were once raised by him and in the course of time developed into true cultivated plants. This transition from wild plant to cultivated form continues right into our time. Thus the corn salad or lamb's lettuce, *Valerianella olitoria,* is a relatively young cultivated plant. A good number of our pharmaceutical herbs are now in transition, heading toward production by planned cultivation. Several tropical plants of worldwide economic importance were originally plants whose useful parts were gathered wild, such as the various trees producing rubber or gutta-percha, the maté plant, *Ilex paraguayensis,* and the numerous species from whose bark quinine is obtained. In the primeval forests these valuable plants decreased more and more because of usually wasteful exploitation, and since, for this reason alone, the increasing demand for these valuable raw materials could no longer be satisfied, they have been raised in plantations for some time.

It is characteristic of plants that have been under culti-vation for only a short time for both stages of exploitation—

the gathering of wild plants and the growing of cultivated forms—frequently to take place simultaneously. A good example is the raspberry, which is harvested both from wild plants in the forest and from cultivated plants in our gardens.

Man gathered and utilized useful parts of various plants for a long time before the idea occurred to him that he could get food much more easily and surely if he sowed or planted these useful plants in a suitable place near his dwelling. He may have been led to this idea by observing that fruits or seeds dropped from wild plants that he had brought home grew into particularly luxurious plants in the rich soil around his dwelling. The accumulation of gathered plants around the dwellings of the Chukchi, a tribe of hunters and foragers of northeastern Asia who live on the Chukchi Peninsula near the Bering Strait, is very clearly described by Maurizio: "The Chukchi gather large supplies of vegetable foodstuffs for the winter. They are, so to speak, unintentional plant breeders. Plants grow densely almost everywhere around their tents; some of them, by chance, find rich nourishment in the refuse, while others owe their location to the Chukchi, having been gathered far away and come to grow in the refuse individually. Among these a cineraria, a composite plant, deserves particular mention, for it is found only around the tents, where it contributes its annual share to the support of the Chukchi."

Such intentional propagation of wild plants first took place in North America, where the Indians sowed wild rice in suitable moist places, not taking any further care of the plants until harvest time. According to Konstantin von Regel, the oak, which, as was mentioned above, served as an important source of flour in prehistoric and even medieval times, was planted near dwellings to make it available in sufficient quantities at any time. The large oak groves that we find today around many farm buildings in Lower

Saxony may be left from those ancient times when acorns still served as human nutriment.

The example of lamb's lettuce shows very well how a gathered plant may gradually become, by planned growth, a cultivated form. In the early eighteenth century, this species, found in fields and on waysides in its wild form all over central Europe, was still a typical gathered plant. From fall to spring its shoots could be gathered in the fields, providing, at a time when there was a scarcity of fresh vegetables, a delicious and vitamin-rich salad. However, gathering such a relatively small plant during bad weather is both troublesome and time consuming. As early as 1701, people were advised to dig up lamb's lettuce or corn salad with its roots in August and to plant it in their gardens, making this much-desired wild vegetable more readily available in winter. The plants developed better in the rich soil of gardens than in the impoverished fields of those days; hence it proved advantageous to grow lamb's lettuce in the garden. And so the gathered plant became a plant grown by man, and, eventually, the cultivated form that we know today.

The sowing of useful wild plants without first tilling the soil or caring for the growing plants is, however, only the first step toward real agriculture. With the following additional steps, man succeeded in creating an environment particularly favorable for plants: preparation of the soil for seed; weeding out of plants not wanted in fields; and fertilization, that is enrichment of the soil by those components that are necessary for growth and development. This made it possible actually to develop particularly productive plants whose valuable properties had been latent. Hence it became feasible for man to develop individual forms having better properties or higher yield capacity from the great mass of wild plants that he cultivated. With the beginning of agriculture—primitive though it was—the conditions for development of true cultivated forms came into being.

DIFFERENCES BETWEEN WILD PLANTS AND CULTIVATED FORMS

Do wild species, if they are grown by man, turn directly into cultivated plants? By no means. The plants remain wild plants even when they are grown under the improved conditions of cultivation, showing better development and a higher yield than those plants gathered in fields and forests. They still have not lost any of the properties that mark them as wild plants and have not yet taken on any characteristics that make them more useful or desirable than wild plants, and so they do not differ in any way from the wild form. They are as useful as gathered plants, but can in no way be considered true cultivated forms, for a genuine cultivated plant always differs from its wild ancestor in certain of its hereditary characters.

THE GIGANTISM OF CULTIVATED PLANTS

If one compares cultivated forms with their wild ancestors, one characteristic that usually differentiates them is immediately striking: this is the difference in structure, especially in size, of wild and cultivated forms. Compared with the smaller and more slender wild species, the cultivated plant always appears larger and more robust. It is a giant plant, called "gigas," a term applied to polyploid plants. This more luxuriant development of cultivated forms is manifested not only in the height of the plants, but also in the development of all their parts. Cultivated plants, as a rule, differ from their wild forms by having larger, and especially broader and thicker, leaves (Fig. 2); sturdier

Fig. 2. Leaves of sorrel, *Rumex acetosa:* (*left*) a cultivated variety; (*center and right*) two wild forms.

sprouts, stems, and stalks; larger and often fleshier roots; and larger flowers (Fig. 3), fructification (Figs. 1, 4, and 6), fruits (Figs. 4, 7, and 14), and seeds.

As is generally known, higher plant forms consist of a great number of elementary units—cells. An increase in the mass of a plant may be the result of an increase in cell size with no change in the number of cells, an increase in the number of cells with no change in cell size, or an increase in both size and number of cells. We know that all three possibilities exist in nature.

Nowadays, we are in a position to make some statements about the real causes of increases in cell size and in number of cells. A frequent cause of gigantism is, as was said before, polyploidy, the doubling or even multiplication of the total

Fig. 3. Blooming fairy primrose (*Primula malacoides*) plants: (*left*) the wild form, introduced into Europe at the beginning of this century; (*right*) a cultivated form derived from the wild form. Large flowers in great numbers were obtained in a relatively short time through planned breeding. (After Böhnert and Mühlendyck)

Fig. 4. (*Left*) Fruit of the wild raspberry *Rubus idaeus* and (*right*) fruit of a cultivated form derived from it, the variety "Preussen."

number of chromosomes, which carry the genes and, in nondividing cells, form the nucleus, which controls metabolism. Cell enlargement due to polyploidy may vary in degree in different cases, but, as a rule, doubling of the chromosomes is accompanied by a doubling of cell volume (Figs. 5 and 6).

However, we do know of gigas plants in which there is no increase in the number of chromosomes but which show, compared to closely related plants, typical gigantism.

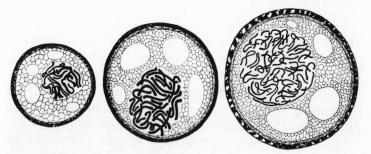

Fig. 5. Increase in size of pollen grains with increasing degree of polyploidy in a tulip variety, "White Duc Maxima," derived from *Tulipa suaveolens:* (*left to right*) nonpolyploid grain with 12 chromosomes; polyploid grain with 24 chromosomes; polyploid grain with 48 chromosomes. (After de Mol)

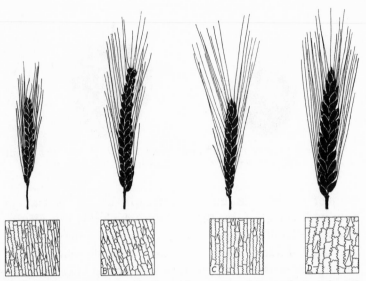

Fig. 6. Size of ears and cells (from the outside of the enclosing glumes) of wild and cultivated forms of wheat: (*left to right*) wild einkorn, *Triticum boeoticum* (14 chromosomes); einkorn, *T. monococcum* (14 chromosomes); wild emmer, *T. dicoccoides* (28 chromosomes); emmer, *T. dicoccum* (28 chromosomes). The figure shows that enlargement of cells and organs takes place during evolution from wild to cultivated form as well as during doubling of chromosomes.

This is especially true of many cultivated plants. If we compare the wild forms of the one-grained emmer or barley with the cultivated plants that are their descendants, we see in both cases that the cultivated forms show gigantism. The same thing is found by comparing the cultivated tomato *Lycopersicon esculentum* with its presumed wild ancestor, *Lycopersicon pimpinellifolium* (Fig. 7), wild and cultivated celery, and numerous ornamental plants having wild original forms with modern commercial varieties (Fig. 3). In all cases, we observe typical gigantism in the cultivated forms, but the numbers of chromosomes of these gigas plants do

Fig. 7. Fructifications (*left*) of the wild tomato species *Lycopersicon pimpinellifolium* and (*right*) of a cultivated variety ("Rheinlands Ruhm") of *L. esculentum.*

not differ at all from those of their wild progenitors, which display no such gigantism. It is true, at least in the majority of such cases, that an important change in the chromosomes seems to have taken place, especially often among nonpolyploid gigas plants, which are considerably larger, and notably thicker, than they are in closely related plants that do not display gigantism (Figs. 8 and 12). According to the English botanist Darlington, the individual genes consist of basic elements called monads. If in certain plants the chromosomes are distinctly thicker than in others, the assumption that the genes in them consist of a larger number of monads is warranted. If this should be true of giant plants with enlarged chromosomes, the operative substance

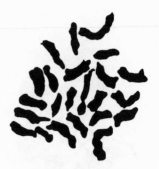

Fig. 8. Increase of chromosome size in nonpolyploid plants: (*left*) chromosomes of the wild tomato species *Lycopersicon pimpinellifolium* and (*right*) of the cultivated variety "Rheinlands Ruhm" of *L. esculentum* (× 3500; after Schwanitz and Pirson).

in the genetic process would be similarly multiplied, as is the case when chromosomes are doubled or multiplied. Then the difference between the two groups of giant forms would be essentially that in polyploids the increase in genes results from an increase in number of chromosomes, whereas in nonpolyploid gigas forms it results from an increase of genes within the chromosomes. The two phenomena, though quite different, would cause an identical change of genetic constitution: they would both effect a quantitative increase of substance in individual genes. Thus it is understandable that in the two cases identical effects are achieved with respect to plant growth: an increase of cell volume resulting either from an increase in the thickness of chromosomes or from multiplication of the number of chromosomes (Fig. 6), these once again leading to the well-known phenomenon of gigantism.

In contrast to the polyploid gigas forms, where gigantism is caused exclusively by an increase in cell volume, in gigantism in nonpolyploid plants the increase in number of cells plays a part, in addition to increase in cell volume, and, as was pointed out above, there even exist gigas plants in which only the number of cells has increased.

THE ADVANTAGE OF GIGANTISM FOR THE SUITABILITY OF A PLANT AS A CULTIVATED FORM

Since gigantism is a rather common phenomenon in cultivated plants, we can assume that it makes such plants particularly suitable for cultivation by man. Such advantages do indeed exist in gigas forms, owing to the increased size of the plants' organs and the resulting increase in yield. In a cultivated plant it is of the utmost importance whether or not the parts actually utilized by man are large or small (Figs. 7 and 10), for the increase in size of the leaves, fruits, and seeds makes harvesting significantly easier. In ornamental garden plants, the size of the flower is an essential characteristic of the cultivated plants (Figs. 3 and 19).

Above all, enlargement of the area of the leaf, an important characteristic of all gigas plants, may have a decisive influence on the yield of the plant. The leaves are the organs which the plant synthesizes carbohydrates, primarily sugar and starch, by means of absorbed solar energy and water and carbon dioxide. In them occurs the synthesis of nitrogen compounds, especially amino acids and proteins. Hence all the essential organic compounds with which the plant builds itself up and which constitute the basis of nutrition for men and animals are produced in the leaves. If, as in the case of commercial plants, the size of the leaves is increased as a result of gigantism, the plant is capable of a correspondingly higher yield: in the same amount of time it can produce more organic material than wild plants, with their essentially smaller leaves, can. Thus the cultivated

plant can, because of the enlarged area of its leaves, produce more material and grow an essentially greater number
of leaves, fruits, and seeds than its wild ancestor.

The higher yield of cultivated plants is also, in forms
having a relatively short time of development, at any rate,
largely determined by the marked increase in the size of the
seeds. A large seed favors rapid and even germination and
speeds up early development. Owing to the larger amount
of nutritional material in larger seeds, young plants have a
much better start, and this more favorable development in
the early stage is followed in the adult stage by earlier ma-
turity, higher yield, and better commercial quality.

Improved quality of harvested products is often a further
result of gigantism, for the increase in size affects different
parts of an organ in different ways. This is most apparent
in the fruits and seeds of our cultivated plants. In wild
forms of apples and pears, for instance, the core and seeds
occupy a relatively large portion of the fruit, whereas in
garden varieties the proportion of the fruit pulp, the part of
the fruit most valuable to us, is much larger (Fig. 15). Very
similar conditions are found in the tomato, in which the
wild form has only a little pulp, the greater part of the fruit
being filled with a gelatinous mass in which the seeds are
embedded; in the cultivated tomato, on the other hand, the
pulpy pericarp of the fruit and the partition between the
two halves of the fruit are very much enlarged and the gelatinous mass containing the seeds makes up a much smaller
portion of the whole fruit (Fig. 9). Moreover, there exist so-
called "beefsteak tomatoes," in which the fruit consists
chiefly of solid fruit pulp. This increase in fruit pulp means
not only an important improvement in taste but also an
increase in the nutritional value of the tomato, for the fruit
pulp contains approximately three times the amount of
vitamin C found in the gelatinous interior of the fruit.

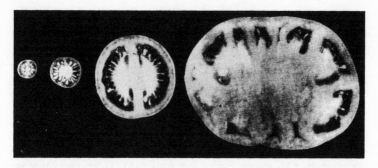

Fig. 9. Proportional sizes of fruit pulp: (*left to right*) the wild tomato, *Lycopersicon pimpinellifolium;* the cherry tomato, a primitive cultivated form, *L. esculentum* var. *cerasiforme;* an ordinary cultivated tomato, *L. esculentum* var. *commune;* and a "beefsteak" tomato.

Hence an increase in the proportion of pulp means at the same time a significant increase in the vitamin content of the tomato. Similarly, in cultivated varieties of the raspberry, the proportion of seeds in individual berries is much smaller than in wild forms, a fact that contributes essentially to the better taste of cultivated raspberries. In strawberries, as is well known, the actual fruits, small "nutlets," or seeds, sit on top of and around the fruit pulp, which consists of the enlarged and fleshy receptacle. The larger the fruit, the smaller the ratio of the number of seeds to the mass of the pulp of the fruit. Thus, with strawberries, the quality of the fruit improves with increased size, since the seeds are not only a nuisance in eating but can, because of their bitter taste, reduce the quality of jam made from the fruit. Here a phenomenon appears that often plays a remarkable role in the improvement of the quality of cultivated plants: the relative decrease of the number of seeds is due to the fact that, with the enlargement of the fruit, the berry's volume increases to a greater extent than its surface, where the actual seeds are located (see Fig. 40).

A similar observation can be made by comparing the wild species of oats and barley with their cultivated forms. In the wild species, the weight of the glumes, which tightly enclose the actual grain, is markedly larger in proportion to the weight of the entire fruitlet than in the cultivated forms. Finally, an analogous condition is found in the seeds of wild and cultivated forms of Leguminosae.

However, improvement of quality through gigantism results not only from the increase in size of the various organs, but in many cases, beyond that, from the increase of the basic units of these organs—the cells. For these, too, it holds true that larger cells have relatively smaller surfaces than smaller cells do. This relative diminution of the surface of larger cells plays a role in the proportion between cell content and cell walls. The smaller the cell, the larger the share its walls in the total substance of the cell, and conversely, the larger the cell, the smaller the role the cell walls play in the material composition of the cell. Cell walls in plants consist of cellulose, a solid substance that is indigestible by man. The larger the proportion of wall substance, the tougher the organs of plants and the more difficult to digest. Therefore it is understandable that the microcellular wild species possess relatively tough organs, whereas those of the macrocellular cultivated forms are much more delicate.

The greater delicacy of usable tissue is also produced by a larger water content of cells, which seems to be characteristic, at any rate, in gigas plants with enlarged cell volume.

DECREASED FRUIT-PRODUCING ABILITY
IN CULTIVATED PLANTS

We know that the polyploid gigas plants are less fruitful than their nonpolyploid original forms. Comparative studies of nonpolyploid cultivated plants and their original wild forms have shown that here, too, gigas plants show decreased fruit-producing ability; as a rule, they produce fewer buds, flowers, fruits, and seeds than their respective wild forms do. At first glance, this decrease in fruitfulness appears to be a gross contradiction to the increase in yield, mentioned above, resulting from gigantism. This is indeed true if only the *number* of fruits and seeds is considered. But if the *weight* of seeds or fruits harvested from wild and from cultivated plants is examined, the picture changes significantly (see Fig. 7), for in this case the gigantic cultivated forms show, as a rule, higher yields, while the more fruitful wild plants are less productive. The cause of this singular phenomenon can be found in the much greater weight of the organs of cultivated forms, which largely compensates for the smaller number of fruits and seeds, or even, beyond this, may lead to yields of cultivated plants— as regards their weight—surpassing by far those of the wild species, as is the case, for instance, with our cereals. The same applies to wild and cultivated flax and to numerous other species.

In some cases, however, the cultivated form shows smaller fruit production than its wild species. This, for example, is the case with the plum, *Prunus domestica*, whose average yield is considerably lower than that of one of its parent species, the cherry plum, *Prunus cerasifera*. Although this species also possesses pleasant-tasting fruit, the size of its fruit and the much better quality of its pulp have caused it to become more common and more highly esteemed than the cherry plum. From this example we can see very clearly that the size and quality of the parts of plants used by man are such important properties of cultivated plants that in certain cases even yield may play a minor role.

Differences in the size of the whole plant and of the organs exist not only among wild species and the cultivated plants derived from them; among cultivated plants, too, gigantism is often found to develop very differently. Thus, the large-seeded oil flaxes, with their large flowers, fruits, and seeds, appear as typical gigas forms compared with the small-flowered, small-seeded fiber flaxes. A comparative investigation of cells and nuclei has shown that the oil flaxes indeed possess larger cells, nuclei, and chromosomes than the fiber flaxes. Quite similar conditions are encountered in various cultivated varieties of the leek, *Allium porrum*. The early "summer" leek has much thinner sprouts and much smaller leaves than the winter variety, which displays, compared with the "summer" leek, typical gigantism (Fig. 10). Here, too, comparative microscopic analysis of

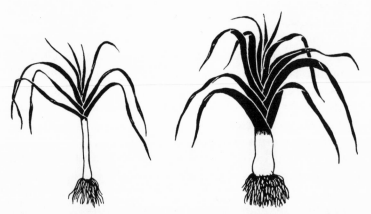

Fig. 10. Differences in the degree of gigantism in cultivated plants: (*left*) "French summer leek," *Allium porrum;* (*right*) winter "elephant" leek.

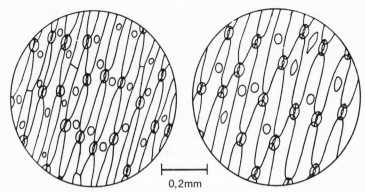

0,2mm

Fig. 11. Cell networks of (*left*) the "French summer leek" and (*right*) the "elephant" variety. (After Schwanitz)

the tissues of the two different varieties shows that the delicate summer variety has small cells with small nuclei and small chromosomes (Figs. 11 and 12), while the gigantism of the winter variety is shown in the size of the cells and

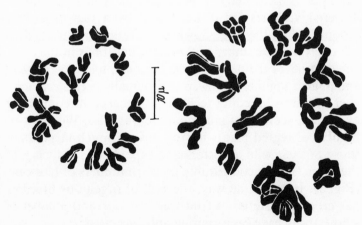

Fig. 12. Chromosomes (*left*) of the small-celled "French summer leek" and (*right*) of the large-celled winter "elephant" variety of *Allium porrum*. (After Schwanitz and Pirson)

chromosomes. Hence gigantism is a property that not only differentiates cultivated plants from wild forms but also can be developed to varying degrees among cultivated plants, bringing about the creation of varieties with widely differing yield capacities, for differences in the extent of gigantism within a given species of cultivated plants affect not only the structure but also the yield capacity of the plant concerned. In the winter leek, the higher degree of gigantism causes slower development and thus an extension of the vegetation period. This in turn causes gigas plants to have more time for assimilation—the formation of organic material by means of solar energy—and is therefore ultimately one of the causes of the higher yield of the gigas plant.

The decrease of fruitfulness connected with gigantism is frequently encountered within individual species of our cultivated plants: for instance, the larger the flowers of our ornamental garden plants, the smaller their number. An example is provided by petunias, in which the small-flowered varieties are distinguished by a rich display of blooms, while the large-flowered varieties produce only a relatively small number of flowers. Conditions in the cultivated forms of the daisy are similar: here, too, large flowers and a large number of flowers are mutually exclusive. However, modern breeding techniques succeed in combining even such seemingly incompatible qualities. We know of highly cultivated plants having flowers much larger than those of their wild ancestors and capable of producing, at the same time, incomparably greater numbers of blossoms (Fig. 3); in the same way, the skill of ingenious breeders has created varieties of fruit trees the size and number of whose fruits have been considerably increased.

As mentioned above, the large-seeded oil flaxes have a more pronounced gigantism than the fiber flaxes. It is significant that the fertility of the oil flaxes is much lower than that of the fiber flaxes. Whereas fiber flaxes have about eight seeds per capsule, the fruits of the oil flaxes contain only about five seeds, on the average. However, the smaller number of seeds in the oil flaxes is compensated by the larger size of the seed: the weight of 1000 seeds of fiber flax is only 5 gm, as compared with 11 gm for oil flax.

We encounter here the same phenomenon that we found earlier in the fruits of the gigas forms: for the survival of a species in nature, it is essential that as many fruits and seeds as possible be produced. The breeder, particularly in the case of those plants whose shoots, roots, or leaves are used, also places special emphasis on harvesting as many seeds as possible from an individual plant. In cases where man himself consumes the fruits and seeds, on the other hand, or uses them in the preparation of food, the bulk—the total weight—of the harvested fruits or seeds is the decisive factor. Here, as we have seen, it is by no means irrelevant whether the higher yield is produced by an increase in the number or in the size of fruits and seeds. In these cultivated plants, large fruits and seeds are highly advantageous to man and hence are frequently found.

We have gone thoroughly into one characteristic in which the wild and the cultivated plant differ basically—gigantism—because we believe that the transition from normal to giant growth is the most important step in the evolution of wild species into cultivated plants. There are various reasons that support this assumption. First, in contrast to other characteristics, there *always* exists a difference in the size of the organs and of the plant, and frequently in the size of the cells, between wild and cultivated plants. Second, gigantism produces, as has been shown, a notable enlargement of those organs of plants used by man; a marked increase in yield; and, above all, significant improve-

ment in the quality of the plant products. All these properties are of paramount importance in the use of the plant by
man; their further improvement, even in cultivated plants,
is still one of the most important tasks of plant breeding.

ALLOMETRIC GROWTH OF ORGANS USED
  IN CULTIVATED PLANTS

To the over-all enlargement of all parts of a cultivated
plant, which we call gigantism, is added another equally
important and characteristic phenomenon: the disproportionate increase in size of the utilized organs. For instance,
if one compares the weights of the leaves and fruit of the
wild red pepper with those of large-fruited cultivated forms
of the same species, one observes that, in the cultivated
form, the leaves are approximately four times as heavy as
those of the wild species, while the weight of the fruit
ranges roughly as high as 500:1. Similar, but not always such
extreme, conditions are found in wild and cultivated forms
of other species such as apples and pears, gooseberries (Fig.
13), and currants.

The disproportionate growth of utilized parts is particularly noticeable in cultivated plants that are grown for their
roots, such as mangel-wurzel (Fig. 20), chicory, radishes,
and carrots (Fig. 18). In the case of ornamental plants, the
flowers and inflorescences are relatively much more enlarged than the leaves, for instance. We may say rather generally that those parts of a plant that make it valuable to
man and for which it is grown undergo enlargement beyond, sometimes far beyond, the over-all gigantism. It seems
that this differential development of those organs especially
valuable to man is a typical character of cultivated plants
that largely determines the plant's yield, and most probably
too the quality of the harvest. Allometric growth of certain

Fig. 13. Branches of (*right*) a wild form and (*left*) a cultivated form of the gooseberry (*Ribes uva-crispa* L.). Note the relatively small increase in leaf size as compared to the marked increase in fruit size.

organs is known from the phylogeny of a series of four plants. Here, with an over-all enlargement of the whole body, certain parts of the plants show a specially conspicuous size increase.

REDUCTION OR LOSS OF NATURAL MEANS OF
DISSEMINATION IN THE CULTIVATED PLANT

For the greater number of wild plants, the survival of the species in nature is ensured by the production of large numbers of fruits or seeds. In order that the fruits and seeds may fulfill their function, all wild plants have mechanisms for dissemination. There are many means of dissemination among individual plant groups. For example, in the legumes and the cress family, because of the special structure of the inner pericarp, tensions result during maturation that lead to breaking up of the shells or pods along the sutures between their two halves. The ripe fruits often burst open with such force that the seeds are widely scattered. In wild species of the poppy and also in the primitive cultivated forms of the oil poppy, scattering of the seeds is ensured, for the walls of the capsules are provided with pores that open when the fruits mature (Fig. 14), so that the seeds can be easily flung out by the wind through the holes in the capsule.

In the wild forms of our cereals, dissemination of the species is provided for in yet another way. In the wild forms of barley, emmer, and rye, the ripe ears shatter into their individual spikelets, which then, together with the grains they hold, are widely scattered by the wind (Fig. 1). The false wild oat—for instance, the fatuoid that grows as a weed in our oat fields and resembles, in certain respects, the original form of the cultivated species—lets its kernels fall off the panicle when they are ripe.

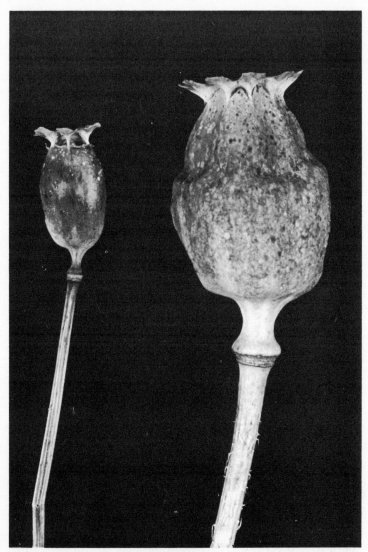

Fig. 14. (*Left*) Capsule of the wild poppy, *Papaver setigerum*, with pores opening when ripe; (*right*) capsule of an opium poppy, *P. somniferum*.

All these mechanisms for dissemination of fruits and seeds are useful and even vital for wild plants, since survival and dissemination of the species depend on them. For man, however, the ability of plants to provide for their own dissemination is not desirable, because in that way he loses a considerable part of the harvest. Hence we find that in almost all important cultivated plants whose fruits and seeds are used, the natural mechanisms of dissemination are missing. Our cereals have a rigid rachis that does not shatter when ripe. In cultivated varieties of flax, the fruit capsules do not shatter, and neither do the pods of our cultivated peas or common field and garden beans. The only cultivated poppy we have is the opium poppy, whose capsules no longer contain any pores through which ripe seed could escape. Only in very primitive field varieties in agriculturally undeveloped regions has the original ability of plants to take care of their own dissemination occasionally been kept even in cultivated plants. Thus, in isolated districts of Spain even today is grown a primitive variety of flax having fruits that burst open when ripe; and every so often we find the black poppy, which scatters its seeds when ripe, like the wild species of poppy. Even in cultivated plants as old as our cereals we encounter an occasional remnant of the ability to provide for distribution of their offspring. For instance, the wheat *Triticum spelta,* or spelt, has a rachis with a certain tendency to shatter, and even in the cultivated oat the tendency of the ripe fruitlets to fall off has not yet been completely eliminated by breeding.

Awns—the long, spinelike, barbed appendages of the glumes, which are bracts enclosing the kernels—probably serve to protect the grains from damage by animals, while aiding dispersal by wind and animals. Most of the cultivated oats do not have awns, whereas wild ones do. Many cultivated varieties of wheat likewise lack awns, and there are even awnless varieties of barley and rye.

Man has also sharply curtailed the natural capacity for dispersal of cultivated plants that reproduce vegetatively. Some species of wild potato grow long underground rhizomes producing tubers that serve for vegetative reproduction at a great distance from the parent plant. Older cultivated varieties also show this same characteristic, which is very important for the dispersal of the plant. The scattered location of the tubers in the ground is rather troublesome to the farmer, however, for it makes harvesting more difficult and expensive. Hence today varieties have been bred that have very short rhizomes so that the tubers are clustered tightly around the base of the shoot.

To the loss of natural means of distribution in cultivated plants is frequently added the loss or deterioration of the natural mechanical protection of fruits and seeds. Take, for instance, the glumes of our cereals, which, in all wild forms, enclose the kernels tightly in order to protect them from damage and animals. Man prefers cereals whose glumes remain on the pedicel, spreading apart when ripe and thus releasing the naked grain. Hence, in most varieties of wheat, rye, and maize we now find such naked or free-threshing varieties exclusively, and even in barley, oats, and millet, which we think of as having hulled kernels, there exist a number of free-threshing varieties.

To these means of protection also belong the thick and solid walls surrounding the seeds of drupes—cherries, plums, apricots, peaches, and walnuts. Here too, in some cases, man has reduced or completely eliminated these troublesome formations. Thus today, in most cultivated forms of the almond, we find drupes with relatively thin walls. In China, there are varieties of walnuts having paper-thin shells. The stoneless plum developed by the American

Fig. 15. There are numerous stone cells in the fruit pulp of the wild pear that are altogether lacking in the cultivated pear.

breeder Burbank, though the seeds are still surrounded by a shell, does not develop stone cells and thus remains soft and gelatinous. In the wild pear, the core is surrounded by a great number of stone cells; in the cultivated pear, at least in choice garden varieties, this growth, which makes eating much less pleasant, no longer exists (Fig. 15). And we should mention the position of the "eyes," or dormant buds, of the potato tuber. In some wild forms and older varieties, they are deeply imbedded in the tuber, and hence are protected. Since deep eyes are hard to peel and cause waste, potatoes with eyes closer to the surface have been developed. For man, all these characteristics are undesirable in cultivated plants. Hence he has, in many cases, taken pains to see that these characters, which lower the quality of plant products for human consumption, were eliminated from the hereditary makeup of his cultivated plants.

With these changes, however, lowering of natural survival and disseminating capacity in cultivated plants has not yet reached the most extreme stage possible.

In apples, pears, figs, and other fruits, there are certain varieties that incline to parthenocarpy, that is, the production of fruits without previous fertilization of the ovules. Although such parthenocarpic fruits still have cores, they are only weakly developed and contain only rudimentary seeds or none at all. A tendency to parthenocarpy is advantageous in plants cultivated for their fruit, for the plants continue to produce fruits even if bad weather or other causes interfere with or make impossible fertilization of the flowers by insects. Hence, pronounced parthenocarpy renders fruit development largely independent of weather and helps to ensure the yield of fruit trees. In addition, cores and seeds are not wanted in fruit grown for human consumption, since seedless fruit is much pleasanter to eat and tastes much better than fruit having normally developed seeds.

Unfortunately, in the varieties of apples and pears that produce fruit by parthenocarpy, the size and quality of the fruit produced without fertilization do not come up to those of normal fruit. In other cases, however, unfertilized fruits develop quite normally. This is true, for instance, of cucumbers; certain varieties of gooseberries, currants, blackberries, grapes, and medlars; oranges, figs, and pineapples; cultivated forms of the breadfruit tree; and all cultivated bananas.

A very peculiar case of a plant's capacity to produce fruit without fertilization is the "vegetative pear," developed by the well-known Russian plant breeder Michurin. This variety blooms like any other pear in the spring, and the fertilized flowers produce normal fruit that ripens in July. After this, the tree blooms a second time, putting forth, in addition, short shoots bearing clusters of leaves at their tips. These clusters thicken at their bases, and each forms a "vegetative fruit" that still bears the cluster of leaves at its tip. This "vegetative fruit" ripens in the fall at the same time as the pears developing from the second flowering.

In ornamental garden plants, the highest development of the flowers also leads to marked, and in certain cases even to complete, sterility. The doubling of flowers, a popular characteristic of many cultivated garden flowers, is frequently achieved by a transformation into petallike formations of those floral parts that determine sexual reproduction—the stamen or even the carpels. The transformation of the reproductive organs of a plant into components of its attraction apparatus can lead to total sterility of the plant. This sterility, however, can be useful in ornamental plants. The double-flowering species and varieties of cherry that are grown in Japan only for their beautiful flowers produce abundant blossoms every year, in contrast to normal trees, for which, as a rule, a year of rich yield is followed by one of sparse production of fruit and flowers. The lack of fructification means that, after flowering, the plant does not consume any nutrients for the formation of fruit.

Just as seedless, parthenocarpic varieties of fruit are the ideal when breeding for choice fruit because seedlessness enhances the quality of the fruit for human consumption, so, too, in ornamental garden plants the sterile varieties, with their double flowers, are considered particularly valuable results of plant breeding, not only for the increased number of petals, but also for the greater abundance of their flowers.

Evolution from deterioration of the capacity for dispersal to its total loss, from a diminished capacity for sexual reproduction to its total failure, culminates in sterile flowers and seedless fruit. The more a plant is improved through breeding and its value for man is increased, the less able it is to perpetuate itself in nature without human care and to transmit its hereditary material and properties to its offspring.

THE LOSS OF BITTER AND TOXIC SUBSTANCES IN CULTIVATED PLANTS

The original, wild species of a great number of cultivated plants exhibit the valuable qualities that distinguish their domesticated descendants. All wild cereals possess good-tasting mealy grains, and, similarly, the seeds of the wild form of the bean *Phaseolus aborigineus* taste so good that they are still gathered in primeval forests. The fruit of the wild tomato is quite palatable even to the sophisticated taste of modern man, and wild strawberries and raspberries are usually considered more choice than the cultivated garden forms derived from them.

However, the wild species that man once used or still gathers cannot always be eaten raw. Many of them contain bad-tasting, unhealthy, or even toxic substances. Of a rough total of 51 plants gathered for food by the aborigines of Australia, only 36 can be eaten raw. None of them is pleasant tasting or of great nutritive value. Nine plants in a second group have roots that are edible if baked. The remaining six plants, which provide the most important vegetable food for the aborigines, are all toxic in the raw state.

In central Europe, both native wild forms of cultivated plants and numerous kinds of fruit gathered by man contain undesirable substances of various sorts. Examples of these are the high tannin content of acorns, blackthorn, crabapples, and wild pears, and the bitter fruit of the wild mountain ash. Great numbers of valuable edible mushrooms, such as various species of Russula and the well-known honey color mushroom, *Armillaria mellea,* are unpalatable if eaten raw, or, like *Gyromitra esculenta,* even toxic. Beechnuts and the berries of the dwarf elder are also toxic.

But primitive man, still in the gathering stage, was able to develop techniques for neutralizing and making palatable the parts of plants that were valuable to him. By chopping up, leaching, drying, roasting, cooking, or fermenting, he could get rid of unpleasant or even harmful substances.

Plants that have been cultivated from time immemorial still exhibit such defects. The raw, immature fruits of the garden bean are toxic, and the numerous techniques used in the Far East for preparing various food from soybeans have as their main function removal of those substances that make the untreated beans harsh-tasting and purgative. In millet, another ancient group of cultivated plants, the grains must be scalded and the water discarded before cooking in order to have a really savory dish.

In most cases, however, cultivated plants no longer contain such distasteful, unhealthy, or even toxic substances, or at least only in very small quantities. Although the fruit of the common bryony tastes bitter, the cultivated forms are free of bitter substances, and only the cucumber, with its tendency to become bitter when its supply of water is insufficient, reminds us of the unpleasant taste of its progenitors. Garden lettuce contains only a small amount of bitter substances, just enough to give it a pleasant and piquant flavor, whereas the compass plant *Lactuca scariola*, from which garden lettuce is commonly thought to have been derived, is disagreeably bitter.

In a good many cases, the degree to which the disagreeable substances in a plant have been removed by breeding is determined by the purpose that the plant serves. An excellent example is the common beet, *Beta vulgaris*. The wild sea beet, *Beta maritima*, contains the highest proportion of substances like saponin and betaine, which give it an unpleasant, bitter, harsh taste. The sugar beet, grown for industrial extraction of raw sugar and not selected for improvement of its flavor, still contains large amounts of these undesirable substances. The different varieties of beets developed for feeding livestock contain much less, and the garden or red beet, bred and grown exclusively for human consumption, can be considered relatively free of undesirable elements.

Actual poisons have even been bred out over the years by man. This is true, for instance, with some important cultivated tropical plants: cassava, various species of yams, and pongamia, all of which contain a hydrocyanic glycoside or some other toxic substance. Such substances make these plants unfit for human consumption unless they have undergone preliminary processing. Since the removal of the toxic substances requires considerable extra work, man has selected from among these plants those forms that are devoid of the substances or have them only in very reduced quantities. Poisonous substances are removed from plants by selection, however, only where they interfere directly with the preparation of food by man. The castor oil plant contains a deadly poison—ricinine—in its seeds, but when the seeds are pressed the poison does not pass out into the oil, which is consequently completely harmless. Since the plant is grown only for its oil, which is used for cooking in the Far East, it has not been considered necessary to breed a nontoxic variety. Indian mustard, or *Brassica juncea,* occasionally sold in European markets as Rumanian or Ethiopian rapeseed, is similar. The seeds of this species contain large quantities of toxic sulfur-containing volatile oils, such as allyl- and croton-mustard oil; when the seeds are pressed they pass into the oil only in small, easily removable quantities. It has so far not been thought worth while to breed nontoxic varieties of Sarepta mustard, and so the content of these two mustard oils is so large that the residue obtained in pressing the oil cannot be fed to livestock.

The disagreeable taste or toxic content that are so disliked by man serve to protect plants from numerous enemies. This is easily seen wherever the bitter variety of lupine, with its alkaloid content, is grown along with the sweet variety, which contains very little bitter alkaloid. If wild animals frequent the fields, one can be sure that they do considerable damage to the area planted with the sweet variety, while adjacent plots planted with bitter lupine remain untouched. Thus, removal of distasteful substances and poisons deprives the plant of its natural means of protection against a number of pests: although it is better suited to the needs of man, it is less fit for the struggle for existence in nature.

THE LOSS OF MECHANICAL MEANS OF PROTECTION IN CULTIVATED PLANTS

The wild plant defends itself against enemies not only by chemical means, but also by a number of mechanical weapons that make it possible to keep off unwelcome visitors. Blackthorns abound with numerous strong thorns that inhibit intrusion and penetration into their shrubs; similarly, wild apple, pear, quince, orange, and lemon trees have more or less well-developed thorns. The fruit of the wild spinach and of some primitive varieties of cultivated spinach are equipped with sharp, prickly outgrowths, while the purebred cultivated forms have rounded fruit cases (Fig. 16). The protection given the fruitlets of both wild and some cultivated forms of cereals by being enclosed in glumes and by the presence of awns has been mentioned. Both the castor-oil plant and most varieties of thornapple have prickly fruit. Since this prickly fruit is hard to harvest, forms without prickles have recently been selected, and are

Fig. 16. (*Left*) Prickly fruit cases of the wild spinach, *Spinacia tetranda*, and (*right*) spineless fruit cases of the cultivated spinach, *S. oleracea.*

now used exclusively in the raising of these valuable medicinal plants. The numerous sturdy prickles of blackberries are also very unpleasant. Thus plant breeding has started to remove these annoying characters of wild plants: we now have some varieties of blackberries without prickles.

THE LOSS OF DELAYED GERMINATION IN CULTIVATED PLANTS

If seeds of wild plants are sown, only a certain, usually rather small, percentage of the seeds germinate immediately after sowing. This phenomenon, called delayed germination, can be due to the presence of substances that inhibit germination of seeds and fruits, which must first be gradually dissolved or decomposed before germination can begin. In other cases, delayed germination is caused by the thickness or impermeability of the shells of seeds or fruit capsules, which inhibits passage of water to the embryo until mechanical damage or the influence of microorganisms makes the protective covering permeable.

Such delayed germination is extraordinarily useful for wild plants, for it has secured the survival of the species in nature. If all seeds germinated as soon as they entered the soil, inclement weather could wipe out all the offspring of a plant or of many or even all the plants of a variety in a larger area. Delayed germination protects plants against this danger. This property is undesirable in cultivated plants, however, where it would consume unnecessarily large amounts of seeds of the variety planted. Delayed germination would also produce germinating remnants in later years that would constantly infect new plantings, as weeds do.

Cultivated plants gave up delayed germination long ago; embryos develop immediately upon sowing in all of them.

By always using seeds from only those plants that develop and are harvested within one year, we have slowly eliminated all varieties having a tendency toward delayed germination.

SIMULTANEOUS RIPENING: A CHARACTERISTIC OF CULTIVATED PLANTS

As the germination of seeds often extends over a long period in wild plants, so does another important process in their life: the ripening of their fruits and seeds. This deferred ripening is peculiarly advantageous for the survival of the species in nature, for in this way the danger of a whole new generation being destroyed by unfavorable weather after germination is considerably lowered.

For man, however, such prolonged ripening would be most troublesome with cultivated plants, since it would mean repeated harvesting of fruit and seeds ripening at different times. Hence we have selected from among the cultivated plants those varieties in which all plants and even all individual fructifications and fruits reach the degree of ripeness required for harvesting at approximately the same time (Fig. 17).

DIFFERENCE IN LIFE SPAN BETWEEN WILD AND CULTIVATED PLANTS

Life span is often one of the characteristics that we change in developing cultivated plants. In many cases it is significantly shorter in cultivated forms than it is in their wild ancestors. Wild rye, for example, is, in contrast to the cultivated annual winter rye, a perennial. But even in cases where wild species are annuals, they often take more time from germination to ripening than their cultivated descend-

Fig. 17. Until recently, the flowers on pea plants were distributed over a large part of the plant, and the peas ripened at widely differing times. In a new breeding variety, the flowers and pods are concentrated in large clusters at the top of the plant. They become ripe at the same time and are much easier to harvest rapidly—special advantages in the field cultivation of peas. (After A. Scheibe)

ants do. Brücher reports that the wild bean *Phaseolus aborigineus* needs much more time to complete its development than the garden bean, *Phaseolus vulgaris,* does. This shortening of development time is characteristic of a number of cultivated plants. We want cultivated plants to achieve what we expect of them in the shortest possible time. The shorter the life span of the plant, the less danger of harm to the crop from pests, infection, or bad weather, and the more certain the yield. Hence breeding of short-lived varieties of oats is being attempted in order to avoid damage by the frit fly. Furthermore, a short-lived variety clears the field at an early time, allowing timely sowing of winter cereals or intercropping, which yields an additional crop between the cereal harvest and the first frost. All these advantages have made fast development and early maturation essential characteristics of numerous cultivated plants.

Shortening of the life span does not always occur in cultivated plants, however. Sometimes, quite to the contrary, the time between sowing and harvesting of seeds is considerably prolonged. Various species used as vegetables are biennials, forming in their first year only leaves, tubers, or thickened roots and not reaching inflorescence before their second year, while the respective wild species either are annuals or occur both as annuals and as biennials. The transition to biennialism rests upon the fact that in these vegetable species prolongation of the life span is very advantageous for their exploitation by man. In all plants whose leaves, tubers, or roots are consumed, these parts will be more succulent the more time they have to develop. Charlock, or wild mustard, is an annual plant that completes its whole life cycle from germination to inflorescence and ripening of seeds in one vegetation period. All the organic substances that are formed must be used up again immediately in order to build up the shoot and its branches, the inflorescence, and, finally, the fruits with their oily seeds—which means that they must especially serve propagation and the survival of the species. The radish, which was probably derived from charlock, is biennial. In the first year, it develops only rich leaves and a large, thickened root, not blooming or fruiting until the second year. Hence the radish is capable of accumulating all of the nutrients formed during the year in its storage organs, the roots, which reach a considerable size and have good nutritional value because of the large amount of organic substance at their disposal. In charlock, however, where the available nutrients are mostly directed to inflorescence, the root is unenlarged, woody, poor in nutrients, and unfit for human consumption (see also Fig. 18).

There exist other varieties of radishes whose fruits and seeds, rather than their roots, are used, for instance, the rat-tailed and the oil radish. The immature fleshy fruit of the rat-tailed radish, which reaches a length of 40–100 cm, is eaten as a vegetable; the oil radish is grown for its seeds, from which cooking oil is produced. In both cases, the parts of the plants that are used are reproductive organs. Hence it would not be expedient to select plants having a prolonged life span, just as it is not with cereals and the garden bean, where rapid development is advantageous because they can be harvested quickly and safely. The rat-tailed and the oil radish, both cultivated forms, are annual plants having a short period of development and unenlarged, hard, and woody roots.

CHANGES IN THE SHAPE OF ROOTS OF
CULTIVATED PLANTS

Plants whose roots are used as vegetables and fodder or—as with sugar beets and large-rooted chicories—by industry have tender and succulent roots of high nutritional value, whereas the original forms of these plants possess hard, dry, thin roots. Thus the shape of roots is important in such plants. This is not the only difference that can be observed between wild and cultivated forms. In all old cultivated forms that we grow for their roots, such as mangelwurzel, turnips, large-rooted chicory, carrots, large-rooted parsley, and parsnips, the roots, as a rule, are not ramified, are relatively short, smooth, and thick, and consequently are easy to harvest; in garden parsley, chicory, and mangelwurzel, however (Fig. 20), we often find long and relatively thin unramified roots. In the wild forms, the very long root usually divides into a number of lateral roots—that is, it is "branched." Such "branched" roots are very useful to the wild plant, for by their ramification the roots are better moored in the soil than is the case with the cultivated plants with their unramified, smooth, and often rather short roots (Fig. 18). Varieties of the same species whose leaves, rather than their roots, are used, are frequently plants having "branched" roots. Here again, man has eliminated characters of wild plants only where they were undesirable in harvesting or eating.

CHANGES IN FLOWERS OF ORNAMENTAL PLANTS

Among cultivated plants, the ornamental plants of gardens and parks have a special place. Although they are cultivated plants, they are not actually useful; their value is purely aesthetic. We enjoy their variety, their sizes and shapes, and the colors and scents of their flowers.

But these plants too, grown only for their aesthetic value, have changed considerably over the course of time. It is likely that man took under cultivation only those species that, even as wild plants, attracted his attention by their

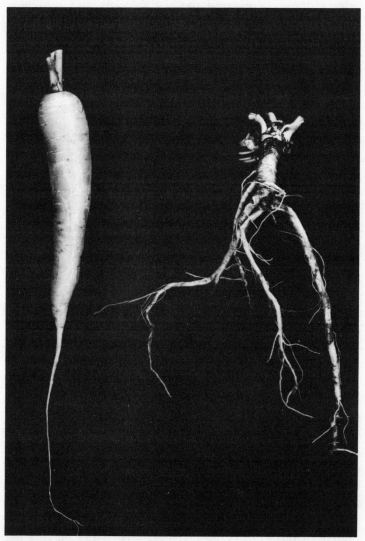

Fig. 18. (*Left*) Root of a cultivated variety of carrot, *Daucus carota;* (*right*) root of a wild form.

beauty, their colors, and the size of their flowers, which have been further developed and improved through cultivation. Thus in ornamental plants too the cultivated forms differ markedly from the original wild species. For the most part they show significantly enlarged flowers and inflorescences, the inflorescences in many cases being doubled ones. This means that the colored parts of the flowers that form the so-called "attraction apparatus" are greatly increased in number.

This doubling of flowers can go so far that the plants are no longer able to reproduce by seeds. Where it is possible to propagate these plants by cuttings or grafting, this sterility may easily increase their value as ornamental plants. Fertilization usually leads to rather rapid withering and dropping of petals. In sterile flowers, the petals last longer and the blooming of individual flowers is considerably prolonged. In addition, plants with sterile flowers do not consume any organic substances for the formation of fruits and seeds, and hence can use all available material for producing flowers. Their blooming is therefore considerably richer, and continues for a much longer time than that of plants having fertile flowers.

The increase in the number of flowers (see Fig. 3) and the lengthened blooming time of individual flowers, of inflorescences, and of the whole plant are important characters in which wild species and cultivated forms, even fertile ornamental plants, differ markedly. Whereas in wild plants individual flowers quickly fade and their petals drop immediately after fertilization, hence causing the inflorescence to look rather insignificant, in cultivated forms hereditary types have been selected whose petals stay on the flower even after fertilization has taken place (Fig. 19), making the inflorescences appear handsome for a relatively long time.

More than anything else, the intensity and richness of the

Fig. 19. (*Left*) Inflorescence of a wild species of larkspur, *Delphinium flexuosum,* and (*right*) of a cultivated garden variety, *D. cultorum.* The small petals of the wild species fall off right after the ovules are fertilized. In the cultivated form, the petals stay on the flowers, fresh and bright, even when the fruits have reached full size.

color of the flowers has been changed in ornamental plants. As a rule, wild species show flowers of only one color, and only rarely do white-flowering varieties of blue- or red-flowering species, or red-flowering varieties of white-flowering forms, indicate the latent capacity of the plants to produce various hues. But what are these unimportant color variations that we observe occasionally in nature compared with the richness of colors in ornamental garden plants, such as the numerous color variations in snapdragons, garden primroses, pansies, roses, and even dahlias!

To this diversity of colors is frequently added a perplexing number of most diverse patterns and wide variation in the shapes of flowers. But even so, this does not exhaust the number of shapes of ornamental plants. There are growth differences ranging from mat-forming dwarf varieties to tall giants, and there exist great differences in development rate from fast-growing forced forms to early-, medium-early-, and late-developing varieties.

Through improvement of the ornamental value of their flowers and an astonishing increase in the diversity of their forms, so rich in shape and color, all the cultivated plants that we call ornamental garden plants have originated from rather homogeneous wild species.

DIVERSITY OF FORMS OF CULTIVATED PLANTS

Increased diversity of forms is, on the whole, one of the most important qualities that distinguish cultivated plants from their wild ancestors. Wild species are always fairly homogeneous, both in the structure of their organs and in their performance. Most wild carrot plants show the greatest similarity in all their essential properties. But what a wealth of different forms is met with in cultivated carrots! They range in size and shape from small, globular carrots to the giant roots of the fodder carrot. Similarly, there is great variation in the color of the roots and in their content of volatile oils, sugars, and vitamins.

The classic example of increase in diversity among cultivated plants, however, is provided by cabbage. Its original form, the field cabbage, which is found along the Atlantic and Mediterranean coasts, is a plant with simple leaves that very much resemble those of rape, which is closely related to it. From this wild form, through the loss of most of the mustard oils, which strongly impaired its taste, and an increase in the number of leaves and their tenderness, came simple cabbages, of which different varieties were known in antiquity. Different varieties of curled kale have evolved through the curling of the leaves of these primitive cabbages, and the enlargement and further increase of the number of leaves has led to the formation of leafy forage cabbages, the kales and the collards. From the latter, with the leaves becoming fleshy and folding up into a head, have evolved the common cabbages: the white cabbage, with its smooth leaves, the inner ones being almost white; the red cabbage, also having smooth leaves, which are stained red by the anthocyan contained in the cell sap; and the Savoy, with curly green leaves, the inner ones being yellowish or whitish.

The fact that head cabbages contain much less provitamin A, chlorophyll, and protein than leafy cabbages has led to the recent breeding, in the United States, of a leafy cabbage with fleshy green leaves. Leafy cabbages, which are particularly striking for their slashed, fringed, and curled leaves, and for being curiously mottled, have been grown for a long time as ornamental plants in gardens and parks.

However, it is not only the leaves that are transformed in garden cabbage; the stem can also undergo considerable change. Kohlrabi originated by a thickening and shortening of the stem. If the stem expands and also becomes fleshy, we get *Markstammkohl,* which is widely used as fodder. And the sprouts, borne in the leaf axils, can develop into small heads; this is how the Brussels sprout originated.

Finally, the flower cluster of the cabbage can also play a part in transformation. It becomes fleshy and we have, if these formations are still relatively loose, broccoli, and, if they are condensed and tight, cauliflower.

It seems that the only part of the cabbage plant that has undergone no change through cultivation is its root, but this assumption is deceptive. Varieties having thickened roots, such as related kinds of turnips, have also been found among the cabbages, but have never been put under cultivation. This is also true of a variety of broccoli whose succulent flower clusters were situated in the leaf axils like the small heads of the Brussels sprout.

A number of varieties of cultivated cabbage that were grown in earlier times, such as Italian broccoli, esteemed by the Romans, who ate only its bleached stems, and a multi-headed variety, no longer exist, but one cannot say exactly why these forms should have disappeared from the ranks of cultivated plants.

This unusually great wealth of different forms in the cabbage is accompanied by variations of numerous other properties. There are winter cabbages, hibernating varieties, forced varieties, early and late varieties, with noticeable differences in shape, size, internal head structure, taste, storability, vitamin and mustard-oil content, and many other important characteristics. All in all, this results in an immense diversity of forms in garden cabbages.

All other cultivated plants follow a similar pattern. Overwhelming diversity in cultivated forms is always opposed by marked homogeneity in wild forms (Fig. 20; see also Fig. 41). This wealth of forms, however, does not manifest

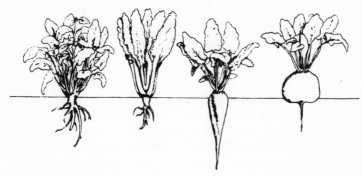

Fig. 20. The most important forms of mangel-wurzel; (*left to right*): sea beet, *Beta maritima; Beta vulgaris:* mangel-wurzel; sugar beet; common beet. (After G. Becker)

itself in all parts of the cultivated plant. It is, rather, only those parts used by man that show the marked variability. Much as the different varieties of cabbage may differ from one another in those organs for which they are grown, the structure of flowers, fruits, and seeds always stays the same.

Ornamental plants, on the other hand, show vast diversity in the structure and color of their flowers. These varieties do not differ very much or at all in other respects. For instance, much as the flowers of snapdragons or of dahlias may differ in form and color among their individual breeds (see Fig. 41), the structure of the stem and the shape of the leaves and seeds is homogeneous even among the most widely differing varieties.

On the other hand, there scarcely exists a part of the plant that has not been recognized as useful in some species and been improved by man. He consumes the ripe fruits of fruits and cereals; in other species—Leguminosae and oil-seeds—he uses the ripe seeds. In other cases, such as beans and garden peas, the immature fruits and seeds are especially valuable. The flower clusters of the cauliflower and the base of the inflorescence of the artichoke are eaten; other flowers are used for the extraction of volatile oils; still others have the exclusive function of being beautiful. In many instances leaves are used for human consumption, as in the various salad, spinach, and leafy vegetable species; in some cases, such as garden cress, only the tender germinal layers are eaten. Frequently roots that have become fleshy are the parts used for human food; in other cases, as with kohlrabi or the leek, it is the tender part of the stem, which is enlarged above the ground, or, as with the onion, the shortened stem under the ground, with its fleshy layers, that is utilized. The tubers of the potato and of the Jerusalem artichoke are thickened parts of the subterranean rhizome. The fibers of the stem of flax and hemp and of the leaves of sisal and the long hairs that clothe the seeds of cotton and kapok are the reasons why these plants are cultivated. Caoutchouc is produced from the milky juice of various euphorbiaceous plants. Turpentine, cedarwood oil, Canada balsam, and balsam of Peru are derived from the resins of various conifers. In short, there is hardly a plant organ that man has not utilized and, in the course of time, transformed to make its usefulness as great as possible.

THE LAW OF HOMOLOGOUS SERIES

Again and again we observe in cultivated plants that, in different species that are even very distantly related, very similar formations occur. Charles Darwin called this phenomenon "parallel variation," while the well-known Russian scientist Vavilov speaks of the "law of homologous series."

We know many such parallel variations, and need mention only a few here. Thus formation of heads occurs in cabbage as well as in lettuce. Curling of leaves is found in cabbage, lettuce, endive, cress, parsley, and celery. Fleshy roots, leaf stalks, and sprouts are seen in plants belonging to very different families.

A particularly remarkable and common kind of parallel variation is the "doubling" of flowers in many ornamental plants. This can happen in many different ways: by division of the original petals; by transformation of the stamens and carpels into petaloid formations; by duplication of the sepals; or by transformation of the sepals into greatly enlarged structures resembling the petals and colored like them. Double flowers originate in the transformation of the inconspicuous small flowers in the center of the capitulum into large and brightly colored labiate or tubulate flowers (see Figs. 28 and 41).

The plant, therefore, can produce double flowers in quite different ways, and this ability occurs in various families among the higher plants. Doubling of flowers is thus a particularly fine example of parallel variation.

It also shows how such parallel variation can originate. It can be shown, in a number of species, that varieties having double flowers are all plants exhibiting gigantism, with enlarged organs and cells (Figs. 21 and 28). The same change in the structure of the plant, gigantism, can thus lead in species of very distantly related families—such as ranunculaceous, composite, rosaceous, and cruciferous plants—to an enlargement of the attraction apparatus of the flowers or of the inflorescences.

Double flowers can arise, as we have seen, from the transformation of stamens into petals. It is obvious that this kind of doubling can result in the formation of beautiful double flowers only in plants that possess a great number of stamens to begin with or that are capable of increasing their number, such as carnations. Such a hereditarily conditioned basis for the increase of numbers of petals exists now in various systematically distant groups of

Fig. 21. Inflorescence and guard cells ($\times$ 500) of the stomata of (*left*) a "semidoubled" and (*right*) a "single-flowered" autumn aster plant. Both plants are derived from the same "double-flowered" parent plant. (After Schwanitz)

plants. Thus there are, among ranunculous, papaveraceous, rosaceous, and malvaceous plants, flowers having a large number of stamens. Hence in all these families, which have no systematic relation to one another, we find hereditary forms having double flowers, the doubling being due to transformation of stamens into petals. In general, this means that certain peculiarities must exist in the structure and function of a plant for certain alterations to occur at all. Since such conditions may prevail among very distantly related species, analogous changes in the life processes or structures of the plants may cause similar new formations in very different species.

However, this phenomenon, while important, is not the only cause of parallel variation. Vavilov has shown that, owing to the descent of many, if not all, higher plants from common original forms, a rather large stock of common genes does exist. By mutation, that is, by hereditary changes of these homologous genes, homologous changes in form could occur in plants belonging to different families. Recent findings in the biochemistry and influence of genes show that Vavilov's conception is probably correct.

WILD-PLANT CHARACTERS IN CULTIVATED PLANTS

It has certainly not escaped the attention of the careful reader that in the preceding sections properties repeatedly named as typical characters of wild plants can still be found today in numerous cultivated plants.

We have seen that the loss of the natural means of dissemination is an essential character of cultivated plants. However, if we take a close look at cultivated plants, we soon discover that in many cases the mechanisms serving the survival of the species in nature have been retained. Rape and turnip are certainly ancient cultivated plants, but nevertheless in these species the pods of nearly all varieties tend to burst open when ripe, and even oats, as mentioned above, show a tendency to "fall off." The cultivated forms of meadow grasses lose their ripe grains as easily as any wild grass, and many vegetables, aromatic herbs, and ornamental plants have preserved the ability of the wild plant to mature their fruits and seeds over a long period and to scatter their seeds widely, causing seed breeders and producers much additional work and expense. It should also be mentioned that the falling of ripe fruit, from apples and pears to black currants, results in material losses from decrease of quality and premature decay, as in the case also of cracking of cherries and tomatoes in rainy periods.

Other wild-plant characters that are closely related to the survival of species are the tight enclosure of grains in glumes in spelt and in most varieties of barley and oats, the sharp awns of ears of barley and rye, and the tendency toward hard seed vessels in the varieties of clover and alfalfa.

Similarly, in respect to distasteful or toxic substances, many cultivated plants even today fail to meet our requirements. Endive, for instance, and chicory still contain an unpleasantly high amount of bitter substances; cucumbers turning bitter during dry spells may well be seen as a remnant of such a wild-plant character. Bitter substances occur in small amounts in oats and barley, and during hot, dry weather the saponin content of spinach may become high enough to cause the leaves to taste disagreeably bitter. In addition to too much saponin in spinach, there are also too many oxalic acid compounds in the leaves. The same holds true of mangel-wurzel, beets, sorrel, and rhubarb. Cabbage varieties, kohlrabi, and turnips contain too much mustard oil and, like Leguminosae, substances of an unknown nature that are detrimental to health. Even some cultivated plants still contain toxic substances. Flax, white clover, and Sudan grass contain hydrocyanic glycosides, which, if the plants are used as fodder, can at least cause forms of rachitis, or rickets. Black currants and quinces have a typical wild-plant character in that they can be eaten only after being cooked.

Another extremely unpleasant wild-plant character of beets should be mentioned here: the growing together of a

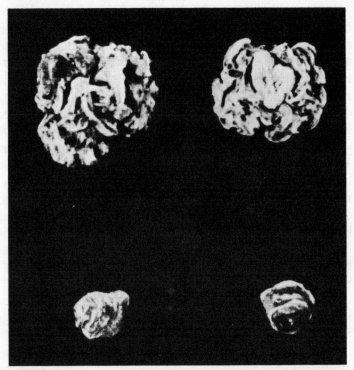

Fig. 22. (*Above*) Normal beet "seed balls" in which a number of fruit-lets have grown tightly together; (*below*) fruits of the "one-seeded" variety.

number of fruits into a "seed ball." In the beet a number of flowers sit close together on one stalk. If fruits develop from the flowers, these grow together, and thus beet coils form in which two to four fruits having one seed each are tightly joined (Fig. 22). The seeds stay in the fruits until germination. Where such a seed ball gets into the soil, a number of seedlings immediately develop very close to one another.

This peculiar "synaptospermy," that is, seeds germinating close to the parent plant, may, under special conditions, be of great value to the wild species. In very dry localities it seems to be more favorable for plants to stand in close groups than to grow in scattered positions. Through synaptospermy, the germination and development of a number of plants close to each other is effected.

As far as cultivated plants are concerned, this character is always undesirable, for it is very unfavorable for root growth if a number of beet plants stay close to one another. To achieve fine, large roots, superfluous small plants must be removed each spring. Since, owing to synaptospermy, the seedlings stand very close to one another, this can be done only by very troublesome and expensive manual labor. Hence today an attempt is being made to get rid of this undesirable formation by mechanical splitting of the coil into its component fruits or by breeding "one-seeded" beets (Fig. 22).

Another wild-plant character of sugar beets is that they sit deep in the soil, which impedes harvesting and causes a dirty crop when the weather is bad.

The following further wild-plant characters in cultivated plants may be mentioned: the toughness of the leaves of winter endive; the hard seed pods of peas and beans; the hard, fibrous layer on the inner pericarp of pea pods; the excessively slow germination of carrot and parsley seeds; the excessively small leaves of many fodder plants. The presence of seeds in most varieties of berries may be taken as a wild-plant character, as well as the successive blooming of blossoms on the same stalk of cut flowers. Thus in many varieties of carnations, for instance, there are on the same stem, in addition to the flower, a number of buds in different stages of development which, once the stem has been cut, fail to bloom.

The existence of properties that are characteristic of wild

plants and are found in many cultivated plants is a consequence of their descent from wild plants. The cultivated plant never originates directly from the wild species in perfect form, but evolves step by step over a long period of time. The farther it has come along, that is, the earlier it was taken under cultivation or the more intensely bred and selected, the fewer wild characters will be found in it. But the younger it is as a cultivated plant, and the less man has tried to improve it through selection, the more strongly certain wild-plant characters will show up in it. Their occurrence in cultivated plants must thus be taken as a sign that a plant has not yet completed its evolution from a wild species to a cultivated plant. The removal of these last remnants of the wild original forms in cultivated plants is an important task of modern plant breeding.

CHAPTER 2

The Genetic Bases of the
Origin of Cultivated Plants

THE INFLUENCE OF GENETIC MATERIAL AND ENVIRONMENT
ON THE PRODUCTIVITY OF CULTIVATED PLANTS

We see over and over again that wild plants brought into
rich soil develop much more fully than in their natural
habitat. When the laws of heredity were still unknown, it
was believed that wild species turned slowly into cultivated
plants under the influence of more favorable conditions. It
was stated, for instance, that the wild carrot would turn
into a true cultivated carrot under continued cultivation in
gardens. Such ideas have never withstood critical examination. Most characters of wild species are not influenced at
all by the external conditions under which the plants live;
only growth, size, and yield of a plant depend on the conditions of nutrition and cultivation, among other things.
But here we have a chance to find out how much the higher
yields obtained from cultivated plants are due to favorable
influences of cultivation and how much they are based on a
favorable change of hereditary constitution.

We can raise a wild plant in cultivated soil and compare
its yield with that of the cultivated form grown in the same
place and then with the yield of the wild species in its
natural habitat. From the differences in the yields of the
wild-growing and the cultivated wild form we can determine the influence of agricultural methods. On the other
hand, the different development of wild and cultivated
plants grown under equally favorable conditions provides

a glimpse of the importance of hereditary constitution in the yield capacity of cultivated plants.

Investigations of this sort have shown that the influence of genes is much less than that of environment in cases where the form concerned has only recently been cultivated and not highly bred, as, for example, in lilies of the valley. For all plants that have been cultivated for longer periods, however, the influence of hereditary constitution on the productivity of the cultivated plant is very great (see Fig. 1). Analysis of these hereditary differences between wild species and the cultivated forms deriving from them makes possible a deeper insight into the origin of cultivated plants and the laws underlying this development. The science of genetics has, in a good number of cases, succeeded in explaining the genetic changes that have caused the transformation of wild forms into cultivated plants.

THE ORIGIN OF CULTIVATED PLANTS BY GENE MUTATION

According to our present knowledge, the transformation of wild plants into cultivated plants results from a substantial change of the hereditary structure of the plant over the course of time. Such changes in hereditary factors are called mutations. The genetic structure of an organism can be changed in many ways, and hence there are a number of rather different mutation processes that have all played a part in the origin of cultivated plants.

First, there are gene mutations, which are hereditary changes of individual genetic factors or genes. Presumably these depend on the changes of the internal structure of the genes, which we now see as large molecules. The various forms of the same genes resulting from mutations are called alleles. Since the function of genetic factors is determined by their structure, any alteration of the structure implies an alteration of the characters that are dependent on these genes.

Such gene mutations occur constantly in all organisms with a fixed but usually insignificant frequency (on an average approximately 0.0005 percent). A large number of the resulting new characters are disadvantageous to the organism. Under natural conditions, this situation leads to their elimination. Occasionally, however, gene mutations do cause alterations that are advantageous to the survival of plants and animals. And there are mutations that, even though they may reduce the survival capacity of a plant in nature, are especially desirable, for they produce those qualities that are the true characters of cultivated plants, as we found in the preceding chapter.

Through the occasional occurrence of favorable characters by gene mutation and the selection of plants having such favorable properties, cultivated species have gradually accumulated more and more valuable characters, and in this way important cultivated plants have originated from a number of wild species. This development is, for the most part, very slow, and it takes hundreds or even thousands of years for wild forms to turn into high-grade cultivated plants. But modern plant breeding has made it possible for us substantially to accelerate this process of transformation, hence making this development a matter of a few decades, rather than centuries.

THE BREEDING OF LUPINES AS A MODEL FOR THE ORIGIN OF A CULTIVATED PLANT

The breeding of lupines provides us with a particularly impressive illustration of the possibility of changing a wild form into a cultivated breed within a short span of time through gene mutation. Here is an example of a cultivated plant that originated within the last 40 years, right before our eyes, and so we can observe closely how the characteristics of the cultivated plant appeared one after the other through gene mutation and, at the same time, how more and more of the wild-plant characters disappeared as the lupine gradually turned into a cultivated plant. Thus the breeding of lupines may serve as a model that can be used to illustrate how old cultivated plants may have evolved from wild species into cultivated forms.

There are three species of lupine grown in Germany that are fit for agricultural use: the white (*Lupinus albus*), the yellow (*L. luteus*), and the blue lupine (*L. angustifolius*), which are all of Mediterranean origin. The white lupine was grown in antiquity, whereas the other two species have been taken under cultivation only recently. In spite of being raised by man, lupines, and especially yellow and blue lupines, can still be considered wild species cultivated by man, since they still preserve, as will be shown, numerous characters that mark them as wild plants.

However, even the short term of cultivation has sufficed to establish a very important character of cultivated plants in lupines: cultivated lupines have attained, in contrast to the wild forms of the Mediterranean region, the gigantism that is typical of cultivated plants. Their seeds are considerably larger than those of wild origin (Fig. 23), and the plants themselves have shown significantly increased growth and more luxuriant development. Gigantism is, as in many other cases, due to an increase of cell size.

How could this important character of a cultivated plant have evolved in such a short time? It is conceivable that man, by repeatedly choosing the largest seeds, has first of all selected individual plants having the hereditary property of producing large seeds, and that from these plants varieties with larger seeds have developed. In this case this

Fig. 23. Seed sizes of wild and cultivated forms of the blue lupine, *Lupinus augustifolius: (left to right)* wild forms from Italy, Palestine, and Spain; cultivated form—normal sweet blue lupine; improved cultivated form—broad-leaved sweet blue lupine. This picture shows that considerable differences in the sizes of seeds may even exist among wild forms.

assumption does not seem to be correct. Originally, lupines were grown as green manure, that is, they were sown solely to produce large amounts of green plant substance to be plowed under for the purpose of enriching the soil with nitrogen and humus. In so doing not much attention was paid to the size of the seeds, but rather to using a variety that would yield as much green plant substance as possible. Therefore, farmers selected lupines to be grown as green manure that would have the greatest feasible growth. In lupine varieties this is largely connected with seed size. Thus a wild Spanish form of the blue lupine has a 1000-grain weight of 94 gm and a height of 60 cm, whereas a cultivated form having a 1000-grain weight of 197 gm grew to almost 90 cm. The selection of plants having especially luxuriant growth brings about at the same time giant forms with particularly large seeds. Figure 23 shows that selection for gigantism is not very difficult, since individual sources of wild forms differentiate according to seed size and thus also according to growth. The tendency to develop giant cells already exists among wild plants; man has only to select the suitable forms from the wild plants accessible to him.

We have seen that gigantism is accompanied, as a rule, by other properties. This is also the case with lupines. Wild forms with small cells possess higher fecundity than the cultivated varieties that descend from them, in which both the number of pods and the number of seeds per pod are reduced. But in spite of the reduced number of seeds, the cultivated variety produces a higher seed yield, from the point of view of total weight, because its seeds are almost three times as large and heavy as those of the wild forms.

The increased seed size also leads to significant improvement in seed quality. As the size increases, the proportion of the hard and indigestible seed coating decreases. Hence in lupines not only the total yield but also the quality of the crop is greatly improved through gigantism.

In the case of lupines, selection of forms for gigantism was a first step toward the evolution of actual cultivated forms. Even so, at this stage of development lupines had to be considered simply as wild forms cultivated by man, for they still possessed a number of rather disagreeable wild-plant characters.

The first of these imperfections was the high alkaloid content of all three species, which made the plants bitter, toxic, and therefore entirely useless as food for domesticated animals. It was known quite early, however, that both in their seeds and in their shoots lupines contain an unusually large amount of biologically high-grade protein, and the yellow lupine was known for its unusual hardiness, so for a long time man wanted to breed cultivated forms from these species. The first step was the removal of the toxic alkaloids.

The first breeder of low-alkaloid lupines, R. von Sengbusch, based his work on some important findings of theoretical biology. From the existence of forms without alkaloids among other legumes, he concluded that, in accordance with the law of parallel variation, low-alkaloid forms should also occur occasionally among lupines. However, from research on mutation he also knew that mutations occur only very infrequently, and that it would thus be necessary to examine a great number of individual plants in order to obtain one low-alkaloid mutant, as the carriers of such mutations are called. By developing techniques that made it possible to examine vast numbers of plants—perfected to such a degree that eventually up to 15,000 individual plants were analyzed by a single person in a day—it was possible to discover in a relatively short time that in the yellow lupine there were three, in the blue two, and in the white one mutant with such a low alkaloid content that all parts of the plants could be eaten readily and without harm by animals.

In this way an important step toward the production of the cultivated plant was accomplished. However, the lupine still possessed numerous other wild-plant characters that were troublesome in the cultivation of this valuable plant. One of these undesirable properties was the cracking of the ripe pods of the yellow and the blue lupines, resulting in the loss of great numbers of seeds. Since closely related plants such as peas, beans, and the white lupine had pods that did not crack, it could be assumed, once more according to the law of parallel variation, that in the yellow and the blue lupine similar mutations could also be found if sufficient numbers of plants were examined. And this proved to be true: from approximately ten million individual plants, von Sengbusch and his colleague Zimmermann discovered a yellow lupine whose pods did not crack when they became ripe (Fig. 24).

But even then the problem of safeguarding the yield was

Fig. 24. The offspring of the first single plant of the yellow lupine (*Lupinus luteus*) having noncracking pods among offspring with cracking pods. (After R. v. Sengbusch and Zimmermann)

not yet completely solved. Although the pods no longer cracked when ripe, they still had another undesirable property: they broke off entirely when ripe. However, the search for plants with pods that did not break off was successful, and a plant could be found whose pods remained firm when mature.

Another wild-plant character encountered in the "sweet" lupine was its tendency to produce hard-coated seeds. When the seeds were stored dry in large quantities, the seed coat hardened so much that it was impermeable by water under normal conditions. Such seeds did not germinate the same year they were sown, but only a year or more later, when the seed coat became chemically or mechanically affected to the point where ground water could penetrate it. The character of being hard coated seems to be very important for the survival of the yellow lupine in native regions. In Palestine, for instance, the vegetation period is followed by a drought that lasts for several months. If the seeds did not possess a tendency to be hard coated, they would germinate during the last rains of the vegetation period and dry up during the following period of drought. They are saved from this fate by their hard coats. During the drought they are cut into during strong winds by sharp-edged grains of sand and thus become permeable, so that at the beginning of the humid season water can penetrate the seed coats to reach and revive the seedlings.

Vital as the tendency to a hard seed coat may be in the wild lupine, it has proved undesirable in the cultivation of lupines, but here, too, it has been possible to find, by methodical selection, mutants that germinate immediately after being sown.

As was mentioned above, the native habitat of the yellow lupine is the relatively dry Mediterranean region. When this species was introduced to the much more humid climate of central Europe, another property was found that might have a quite unfavorable effect, even though it was not harmful in its home region. The pods of the yellow lupine are densely covered with hair. During rainy weather the hair holds the humidity for a long time, so that the pods dry very slowly. In a humid climate this affects somewhat the quality and the germinating power of the seeds. Through selection of mutants that have short hair or drop their hair shortly before ripening, the cultivation of lupines has become more reliable in humid regions. The adaptation of cultivated forms to climatic conditions has been improved further by the discovery of another hereditary form: the fructifications, which are seated deep between the leaves and lateral shoots in the original forms, are high above the foliage, where they can dry and ripen much better.

A cultivated plant cannot demand excessively partial conditions of soil and climate, for this would greatly restrict its cultivation. The yellow lupine was at first very sensitive to soils having too high a water or lime content. A mutant with white seeds proved to adapt itself much more readily to these soil factors than the normal form. Through this mutant and the two others described above, the restriction of the yellow lupine to specific, narrowly defined conditions of soil and climate has been lifted, and hence the usefulness of this plant as a cultivated form has been considerably improved.

On the other hand, the light color of the seed in the white-seeded mutant implies an increase in the value of the lupine as a cultivated plant, for we prefer light-colored seeds for aesthetic reasons and probably also because of flavor, for it has been proved in a number of pulses, as well as in other cultivated plants, that darker seeds do not have as pleasant a taste as light ones. Also, in the white-seeded lupine the biological value of the seed protein is increased.

Furthermore, in all three species of lupines new hereditary varieties were found that excelled in especially rapid early development or in increased growth. Both virtues are important for a cultivated plant, for they enable the plants to cover the soil quickly, suppressing rising weeds and thus requiring less hoeing. Moreover, rapidly developing plants producing large masses of leaves can also be expected to produce high yields.

Up to now, a less desirable property of the lupine has been its tendency to produce, in addition to the main inflorescence and fructification, lateral branches that also bear flowers and fruits. The fruits on the lateral branches ripened much later than those on the principal stalk. This caused harvesting difficulties, since one was forced either to harvest when the seeds of the main inflorescence were ripe or to wait until the fruits on the lateral branches had reached an adequate degree of ripeness. In the first case, immature fruits containing much water would get into the crop, which would consequently dry badly and spoil easily. If the harvesting was postponed until the pods on the lateral branches had reached sufficient ripeness, the pods on the principal stalks were exposed too long to the inclemencies of weather which also led to losses due to falling off, germination, or infection of the protein-rich, sensitive seeds by fungi and bacteria. A successful search for nonbranching plants having only one fructification eliminated this inconvenience, too.

Most important in the breeding of lupines today is the creation of varieties that are resistant to the greatest range of diseases. The survival of species in nature is not generally endangered by their susceptibility to diseases and pests, since only a small percentage of infected plants fail to reproduce or die. Moreover, the scattered distribution of the individual plants means that disease spreads slowly and incidentally. In fields where cultivated plants grow in dense crops, infection and pests can spread rapidly and even take on an epidemic character. A decrease in yield, which is easily brought on by plant diseases, leads to substantial economic loss and makes cultivation unprofitable. Hence the breeding of disease-resistant varieties is as necessary for the lupine as it is for all other cultivated plants, if we attach any importance to achieving a high and assured yield.

By well-planned application of our knowledge of genetics, we have accelerated enormously the transformation of the lupine into a cultivated plant. In the same way, but much more slowly, this process has taken place in the evolution of the older cultivated plants.

THE ORIGIN OF THE VARIOUS FORMS OF CULTIVATED
CABBAGE THROUGH GENE MUTATION

For this slower process, the origin of the various forms of cabbage is a very clear illustration. The raising of cabbage evidently dates from very early times, as has been proved by the discovery of cabbage seeds in the neolithic lake dwellings at Robenhausen. How the cabbages looked we do not know, but they must have been quite closely related to the wild form, if the wild form was not what was actually being planted. In addition to knowing the wild form, the ancient Greeks in the fourth century B.C. were acquainted with two cultured forms of leaf cabbages similar to our kale —a cabbage with smooth leaves, and one with curled leaves. Cabbage was popular with the Romans. Besides the curly cabbage, which they called Sabellic cabbage, they had the Tritianic cabbage, a kind of Italian broccoli, and the Arician cabbage, whose sprouts, borne in the axils of the leaves, were eaten—a primitive kind of Brussels sprout that did not yet show a tendency to fold into small heads. Indeed, the ancients did not know of any head cabbages. In the lettuce-like cabbage, the leaves surrounded the stalk so densely that a headlike formation resulted, but this cabbage, which may well be considered a forerunner of the head cabbages, did not yet possess really compact heads with folded leaves. The Cuman cabbage may be considered similar to our Savoy cabbage, but also without an actual head formation; in the Pompeiian cabbage, the first step toward the formation of kohlrabi is seen.

This development toward the cabbage forms that are known today, which had its first beginnings in ancient Rome, continued through medieval to modern times. In the capitulary of Charlemagne, a primitive form of kohlrabi is mentioned as *ravacaulus;* in the twelfth century, St. Hildegarde of Bingen was acquainted with head cabbages, the white as well as the red. Savoy cabbage is mentioned first by Tabernaemontanus at the beginning of the seventeenth century (its name "Savoy" indicating the area in which it may have originated). The cauliflower comes from the eastern Mediterranean region, having evolved into its present shape from broccoli, a primitive, still very loose form of cauliflower. It was introduced into Germany by way of Italy at the turn of the sixteenth century. The youngest of the cabbage forms is the Brussels sprout, which originated in Belgium at the end of the eighteenth century.

All these various forms of cabbage that we know today have therefore evolved, in the course of several thousand years, from the wild form. Even when specific forms already existed, such as kohlrabi or head cabbage, they did not yet show the shape and yield capacity that is known today. From old descriptions and contemporary illustrations we know that they have slowly evolved from relatively simple original forms and have steadily improved (Fig. 25). By continued selection of the finest and most productive plants, a process that in part has gone on for many centuries, those

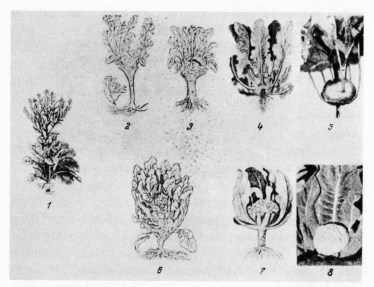

Fig. 25. The gradual perfection of kohlrabi and cauliflower over the course of the past centuries as shown in contemporary illustrations. (After G. Becker)

properties that today are typical of the various cabbages have evolved from the first beginnings of certain characters. Thus a wealth of diverse forms has evolved from homogeneous wild original material.

This slow transformation of the wild form into a cultivated plant, its division over the course of time into a number of highly diverse varieties, and their slowly progressing improvement have become clear to us through the results of numerous genetic studies. Crossing various forms of cabbage with one another has shown that a number of important characters specific to individual varieties of cabbage depend on several hereditary factors that complement each other. Thus the formation of the head in head cabbages and the curliness of kale are each dependent on three different genes. This fact makes it clear that in the cabbage the typical characters of individual forms progressed slowly into the formation known to us today. The hereditary change of one of the three head-formation genes may, for example, have led to the beginning of head formation as described in the time of the Roman Empire. This new variation was recognized as being valuable and was taken under cultivation. In the course of time, another gene in this new variety may have mutated, also bringing about a disposition toward head formation. Since now two genes were present that acted in the same direction and mutually reinforced their effect in this plant, the development of the head was essentially improved. And when a third gene mutated in this plant in such a way as to produce head formation, the "head" of the cultivated plant became as well developed and compact as we know it today. In a very similar way we can imagine the origin and gradual improvement of numerous other cultivated plants.

Genetic analysis of many other plants has shown that here too the origin of characters typical of cultivated plants is based on gene mutation. Some further examples may illustrate this. We have seen that in all cereals the firmness of the rachis is an important character of cultivated forms, while all wild forms possess brittle ears. Crossing cultivated forms of barley with the wild species showed that these have two or even three genes that cause them to be deciduous, scattering their seeds when ripe. If only a single one of these genes is changed by mutation, ears with a comparatively rigid rachis will be formed. Their rigidity will be increased, however, if another gene, or even the two other ones, are transformed by mutation into alleles that accentuate the rigidity of the rachis. From this result we may conclude that the rigid rachis of cultivated barley came about through mutation, in early times, of one of the wild genes causing the fragility of the rachis, and that this favorable mutation was discovered by man and systematically propagated.

We have seen repeatedly that gigantism must be regarded as a basic criterion of cultivated plants. For this specific character, which is so significant in the performance of cultivated plants, it could be shown that it can originate through the mutation of a single gene, as in a giant variety of red clover. Furthermore, a gigas mutant seems to be involved in the case of the well-known variety of coffee, maragogipe, which resulted from mutation in Brazil in 1876, differing from its original form by having much larger beans and decreased fertility.

Finally, the wealth of different breeding varieties of a number of ornamental garden flowers—snapdragon, sweet-pea, stock, and Chinese primrose—is due to gene mutation. Often the history of these species permits us to see clearly how one new character after another has appeared in the course of cultivation, and how, by constant mutation from the extremely homogeneous original form, the great diversity of forms and splendor of colors of modern breeding forms have evolved.

The importance that gene mutation has had for the origin of cultivated plants and that it still has for their perfection is demonstrated most impressively in cultivated garden plants that reproduce by bulbs, tubers, cuttings, or grafts rather than by seeds. In such plants, hereditary changes in form or performance can occur only by a mutation taking place in the young tissue of the growing plant in some cell close to the growing point. All cells and tissues derived from such a mutated cell also contain the changed gene, and hence show altered behavior of the character that depends upon this gene (Fig. 26). Such somatic or bud mutations, called "sports" by gardeners, have led to the origin of numerous

Fig. 26. Somatic mutation in the color of the common dahlia, *Dahlia variabilis:* (*center*) normal form; (*right*) mutated flower.

new varieties. Many new breeds of chrysanthemums,
dahlias, tulips, and hyacinths have originated in this way
(Fig. 27). We know of as many as forty to fifty new varieties
of tulips that have resulted in this manner. The ability to
produce double flowers can also be induced by bud mutation. Figure 28 shows the compound inflorescence of a
single-flowered plant of the China aster, *Callistephus chinensis,* in which, by somatic mutation at many small flower
heads, quite a number of flowers have been changed from

Fig. 27. Somatic mutation in a "forced" tulip variety, resulting in an
economically significant shortening of the time needed for forcing:
(*left*) the normal form; (*right*) the early-flowering mutant under identical conditions. (After de Mol)

Fig. 28. Somatic mutation in the China aster (*Callistephus chinensis*). (*Below*) Cells of (*left*) single-flowered and (*right*) double-flowered heads.

inconspicuous tubes into many-colored, large, labial flowers. Most significant, and proving once more the correlation between gigantism and the doubling of flowers, is the fact that the parts of the double-flowered small heads always have distinctly larger cells than the single-flowered parts. Evidently, in this case, a mutation inducing an increase in cell size causes the formation of double flowers at the same time.

Similar to ornamental plants are the varieties of fruit. The red Gravenstein, for instance, arose as a sport from the yellow Gravenstein early in the nineteenth century. The fact that nearly 400 apple bud mutations were found up to 1936 in the United States alone shows the frequency with which this kind of mutation occurs. The economic value of forms originating in this fashion is shown by the fact that about a third of the patented fruit varieties in the United States have arisen by somatic mutation.

Many of these bud mutations produce changes in the fruits themselves (Fig. 29), but there are mutations that are known to differ from the original form by earlier or later ripening, the capacity to germinate after self-fertilization, the property of producing a full crop every year, and resistance to disease. It is obvious that the value of varieties can be considerably increased by the occurrence of such useful mutations. The particular importance of bud mutation to fruits and ornamental plants lies in the fact that only one character is changed, while the otherwise valuable total character of the variety is maintained unaltered.

The great significance of gene mutations in cultivated

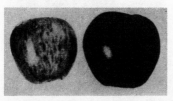

Fig. 29. Somatic mutation leading to a dark red color in the winesap apple: (*left*) fruit of the original variety; (*right*) fruit of the mutant. (After Shamel and Pommeroy from M. Schmidt.)

Fig. 30. (*Above*) Mutant of "Haisa" barley with naked grains; (*below*) grains of the normal form with glumes. (After H. Stubbe)

plants has been confirmed by experimental research. The
rate of mutation can be markedly increased by the use of
X-rays or radioactive isotopes. So far among mutants produced in this fashion, a good number of forms have been
found in which essential characters have been improved by
mutation. In barley, for instance, naked-grained (Fig. 30),
large-grained (Fig. 31), bearded and unbearded, disease-
resistant, early-ripening, and rigidity mutants could be found
after exposure to X-rays. By the same method, varieties of
wheat with increased frost resistance and improved baking
and storing properties have been developed. Induced mutation has resulted in an increase of up to 30 percent in the
yield of barley and some other cultivated plants. A number of
interesting and probably economically valuable mutants
induced by X-rays have been found in the tomato (Figs. 32
and 33) and in red clover. The red-clover mutant is especially remarkable, since it differs from the original form by
marked gigantism.

These results of mutation studies show why modern plant

Fig. 31. Large-grained mutant (*right*) of "Haisa" barley. (After H.
Stubbe)

Fig. 32. Flower (*left*) of a normal cultivated tomato and (*right*) of a large-flowering X-ray mutant of the same variety. The gigantism effected by mutation has resulted in an increase not only in the size of the flower but also in the number of petals. (After H. Stubbe)

breeding is making much greater use of experimentally induced mutation to further increase the efficiency of cultivated plants.

COMBINATION AND NEW FORMATION OF CULTIVATED PLANT CHARACTERS BY CROSSBREEDING

In addition to gene mutation, crossbreeding of different races and species plays an important role in the origin and

Fig. 33. (*Left*) Fructification of a normal cultivated tomato and (*right*) a very much enlarged fructification of an X-ray mutant. (After H. Stubbe)

development of cultivated plants. With the slow rate of gene mutation, it would take a long time for another favorable character to appear in a new, favorable mutant by gene mutation. But the evolution of a cultivated plant can be accelerated by several favorable mutations occurring at the same time in different plants in the same field and being combined through spontaneous cross-fertilization. Such crossing occurs constantly in nature in most plants to a certain degree, and must be considered an essential factor in the evolution of cultivated plants.

This is shown most impressively in alfalfa. The common blue-flowered alfalfa, *Medicago sativa,* which today ranks among the most important green forage, came originally from Asia Minor. From there it went, in ancient times, to the Mediterranean region, and then in the seventeenth century to Germany by way of France, where it spread abundantly during the eighteenth century. But common alfalfa could not survive the colder winters of central Europe, which is easily understandable because of the milder climate of its native region and principal dissemination up to that time, and so it easily perished during the winter. However, in central Europe it met with another, closely related species, yellow-flowered alfalfa, *Medicago falcata,* which, being an indigenous wild species, was excellently adapted to climatic conditions there. The two species hybridized readily, and from numerous spontaneous crossings a multitude of hybrid forms originated that are referred to as variegated or sand alfalfa, *Medicago sativa media* var., and from which, in the course of time, some field varieties developed. These latter combined the large and full growth of blue-flowered alfalfa with the winter hardiness and insensitivity of yellow-flowered alfalfa.

With the origin of these field varieties, capable of enduring German winters, the hybrid alfalfa had not yet exhausted its latent capacity to adapt itself to extreme climatic conditions. In the middle of the last century, a German emigrant named Wendolin Grimm imported seeds of the Franconian variegated alfalfa to Minnesota, but even it could not resist the severe climate of this region, and year after year most of the plants were killed during the winter. The seeds yielded by the few surviving plants were sown again; from the next generation the most frost-resistant types were selected, until finally a hybrid alfalfa was created, Grimm alfalfa, which far surpassed the original form in frost resistance. With the help of this alfalfa, it was possible to extend the cultivation of alfalfa into the far northern United States. It is certain in this case that it was the cross between the two species of alfalfa that resulted in the formation of the prerequisites for the plant's great adaptability to deep winter cold, especially to hoarfrost.

The process of transforming wild species into cultivated forms is markedly accelerated when man looks wisely for useful mutants and combines favorable characters through purposeful crossbreeding. Where this is the case—as with the "sweet" lupine—the transformation from wild species to cultivated plant can be accomplished within a few decades instead of taking centuries or thousands of years.

How much the value of old cultivated plants can be improved by the combination of favorable characters may be shown by an example. Some decades ago, in a variety of common tobacco, "Maryland Mammoth," a so-called short-day mutant had appeared, a form that failed to bloom in the longer day that is characteristic of our latitudes during summer. Owing to this failure, the mutant produced many more leaves than the original form, since it could use all the substances at its disposal for the formation of foliage, the part of the tobacco plant that is used. Possessing this capacity for gigantism during long-day conditions, the mutant could have gained great economic importance if it

had not, at the same time, shown another character that
curtailed its value greatly. It ripened quite late, its leaves
thus failing to turn yellow until late fall, and hence failed to
reach the degree of ripeness necessary for the production of
high-quality tobacco. Then the mutant was crossed with an
early-ripening variety, and the breeder succeeded in select-
ing from the offspring of this crossbreeding plants that
combined the economically important characters of straight
vegetative development under long-day conditions with the
equally important character of early ripening of the leaves.
Only through this combination of the valuable characters of
two different varieties did the mutant Maryland Mammoth
become genuinely economically useful. Here we have an
impressive example of how a mutation that is at first useless
can lead, by combination with another, supplementary
character, to considerable improvement of the plant in
question. Such combination and accumulation of valuable
characters in one plant or variety by crossbreeding the carriers of these characters is an important method of modern
plant breeding and is also one of the decisive factors in the
great success that plant breeding has achieved in the past
several decades.

On the other hand, totally new characters can appear
through crossbreeding different races and species, which
also raise the value of plants for man. We have already
discussed the significance of gigantism in the origin of cultivated plants and have seen that this character can be the
result of gene mutation. It has also been proved that forms
exhibiting gigantism can result from crossbreeding closely
related plants. Thus a gigas oat has been found among the
offspring of a cross between two varieties having quite
normal growth. A similar case is known for the apple. The
crossbreeding of two wild species of apples having very
small fruits yielded a whole series of large-fruited descend-

ants (Fig. 34). [Similar results of crossbreeding wild species of blueberries are shown in Fig. 35.] It must be noted that the origin of gigantism by crossbreeding is caused by both parents' possessing genes for gigantism that by themselves would not produce gigantism. In the offspring of the cross-bred plants, the different genes that complement each other come together to produce the character of gigantism.

Evidently red cabbage originated in quite a similar way. Various purely green cabbage forms possess genes for the formation of anthocyan, which causes red coloring of the leaves. These genes, however, cannot manifest themselves, since they are not complete. If, however, two green varieties are crossed, and one of them possesses the genes that the other one lacks for the production of the red, then among the offspring of such a cross plants containing all the genes necessary for the formation of anthocyan will occur and will have brightly colored red leaves.

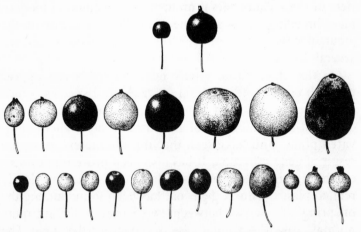

Fig. 34. Occurrence of large-fruited forms among the offspring of a cross between two small-fruited species of apples, *Malus baccata* (*above, left*) and *M. prunifolia* (*above, right*). (After W. Henning)

Fig. 35. The cultivated American blueberry is derived from hybrids of various wild species. Its valuable characters may well be due to the combination of favorable genes of the parent species. (*Left*) Fruits of one of the wild species; (*right*) fruits of a cultivated variety. (After Darrow)

A turnip-shaped, thickened, fleshy root is an important character of many cultivated plants. Crossing a tall-growing variety and a shrubby variety of the scarlet runner bean, *Phaseolus coccineus,* shows very clearly that this character, too, which alone renders many plants useful to man, can be brought about by hybridization. In this case, in the second generation after crossbreeding, roughly 10 percent of the plants appeared with turnip-shaped roots weighing up to three-quarters of a pound and having a good taste and high protein content. Here, as in other cultivated plants—such as the garden carrot, which is assumed to be the result of crossing various wild species of carrots—the ability to form a thickened root may have originated from the combination of complementary genes for the formation of a fleshy root that was passed on by different parents to hybrid plants.

Maize also owes its great yield capacity and vast diversity of forms to the crossbreeding of species. Primitive cultivated forms of this species were introduced from their original homes in the Bolivian and Peruvian Andes into Central America before the discovery of North America and spontaneously interbred there with closely related wild species belonging to the genus *Tripsacum.* Apparently this crossbreeding resulted in a combination of especially favorable genes from both parent species, making possible the high yields that make maize one of the most important plants in the modern world economy.

A multitude of new cultivated plants, most of which are still scarcely known in Europe, have resulted from the hybridization of various species of the genus *Citrus*—to which the lemon, orange, tangerine, and grapefruit belong—with the species of four related genera. Figure 36, which gives only a graphic representation of the genus hybrids, shows that not only the pure species, but also the hybrids themselves, have taken part in further hybridizations, and thus have participated intensively in the formation of a large number of new cultivated forms.

Various European fruit varieties are also the result of crosses between different species: apple and pear varieties, as well as varieties of the cultivated currant, are the products of the hybridization of a large number of wild species. More than anything else, the crossbreeding of species is in many cases the principal cause of diversity of form and color in ornamental garden plants. Offspring with double flowers originated from the hybridization of two species of tobacco. The familiar multicolored cultivated garden petunia, *Petunia hybrida,* is derived from the white-flowering *P. nyctinaginiflora* and the pink-violet *P. violacea.* In cultivated verbena, as many as three or four wild species are combined, and the same is true of the cultivated pansy. The cultivated auricula is a hybrid of the wild form, *Primula auricula,* and the hairy primrose, *P. hirsuta,* while the variegated spring primrose of our gardens, *P. anglica,*

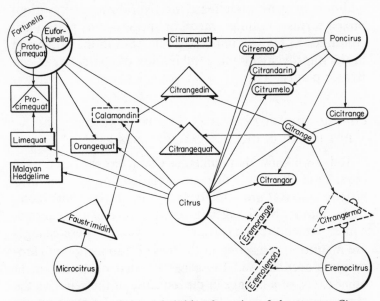

Fig. 36. Diagram of genus hybrids of species of the genera *Citrus, Fortunella, Poncirus, Microcitrus,* and *Eremocitrus.* The five genera are represented by circles, and the two circles within the larger circle of the genus *Fortunella* represent two subgenera. The names of hybrids between two genera are enclosed in rectangles if one of the parents belongs to the genus *Fortunella,* and in ellipses if this is not the case. The names of hybrids of species belonging to three genera are enclosed in triangles if species of the genus *Fortunella* have participated in the breeding of the hybrid, or in a triangle with a circle on each side if *Fortunella* was not involved. Chance seedlings of uncertain ancestry are surrounded by dotted lines. (After W. T. Swingle)

owes its wealth of form and color to a cross between the common primrose, *P. vulgaris,* and the spring primrose, *P. veris.* In addition, a multitude of other popular varieties have resulted from crossing numerous other species of primroses. Crossbreeding of species has also resulted in new cultivated varieties of phlox, peonies, lilies, daffodils, and iris.

The few examples that we have given here show that, in

addition to gene mutations, the hybridization of various mixed forms—families, races, or species—has played and continues to play an important role both in the origin and in the improvement and combination of characters of cultivated plants.

CHROMOSOME MUTATIONS AS EFFECTIVE FACTORS IN THE ORIGIN OF CULTIVATED PLANTS

Today we know that numerous characters that used to be considered the result of gene mutations because of their genetic behavior are actually caused by chromosome mutations, that is, by changes in the structure of the chromosomes, which are the carriers of the genes. These changes are manifold, consisting in the loss or duplication of chromosome sections and the genes situated on them, or, in other cases, of a change in the sequence of the genes on the chromosomes or in the transfer of sections of one chromosome onto another chromosome. These chromosome mutations can, as shown in Fig. 37, cause significant changes in the phenotype of plants, especially changes of the kind known to us as characteristics of certain varieties or even species. Barley mutants with short straw and erect, compact ears, in shape resembling certain varieties of cultivated barley, result from the exchange of chromosome sections between two different chromosomes, and it seems that chromosome mutations have also caused the origin of a few species of wheat.

THE NATURE AND FORMS OF POLYPLOIDY

In preceding sections we have seen that gigantism is an essential character of all cultivated plants. There can take place in the hereditary constitution of plants a change that

Fig. 37. Chromosome mutation in common wheat, *Triticum aestivum:*
(*left*) normally shaped ear of the variety "Scandia"; (*center*) speltoid
mutant of the same variety resulting from a duplication of one section
of a chromosome; (*right*) "compactoid" type caused by a loss of one
section of a chromosome. (After McKay, from Kappert)

nearly always results in the origin of gigas characters, or
polyploidy. By "polyploidy," which is probably best para-
phrased as "multiplication," we denote the phenomenon of
duplication or multiplication of one or both of the two homologous sets of chromosomes contained in every somatic
cell of higher plants. If both sets undergo multiplication,
polyploid plants with an even number of chromosome sets
result. Such polyploids, having four, six, eight or more sets

of chromosomes, are fertile and can be propagated from seeds (see Fig. 5). Another situation exists in polyploids having an odd number of chromosome sets. These forms are largely or even completely sterile and cannot produce homogeneous offspring from seeds. They can, however, be of importance in those cultivated plants that are propagated vegetatively, that is, by grafts, cuttings, tubers, rhizomes, or runners.

Further, we must distinguish between autopolyploid and allopolyploid plants. Autopolyploid plants are those that originate from an increase in the number of chromosomes of a pure species. We can also speak of autopolyploidy if the polyploids in question are derived from a fertile hybrid of different races or even of different species. Allopolyploids, on the other hand, originate from the duplication of the number of chromosomes in a sterile hybrid that comes from two different species, whereby the previously sterile species hybrids become fertile again and reproduce, with all their specific characters, by seeds. Allopolyploids are essentially species hybrids that have become permanent and that differ from their parent species so greatly that they have the character of an independent species. There are also among autopolyploids forms that are considered independent species—this is evidently the case when they are derived from fertile species hybrids—but in most cases they are to be regarded merely as polyploid races.

Identifying a plant as polyploid and determining whether it is autopolyploid or allopolyploid can be done by various genetic means. Thus we can ascertain the kind and degree of polyploidy by examining the number, shape, and structure of chromosomes, by analyzing the inheritance of individual characters, by crossbreeding the polyploid forms with their presumed parent species and then analyzing the character of the chromosome sets in the hybrids, and, above all, by repeating the synthesis of the polyploids from the parent species with a high assurance of reliability. We can even state from which parent species a given allopolyploid plant has arisen.

As new gene and chromosome mutations constantly occur in nature, so too do polyploid forms occur spontaneously over and over again. Thus polyploidy is a very common phenomenon in the plant kingdom. In central Europe, 48.6 percent of higher-plant species are polyploid, and 8.8 percent contain both nonpolyploid and polyploid races. In cultivated plants the percentage of polyploids is even quite a bit higher than in wild species. This indeed shows that polyploidy obviously favors the origin of characters of cultivated plants.

POLYPLOID CULTIVATED PLANTS

By means of various genetic methods, it has been ascertained that a number of important cultivated plants are autopolyploid. They include, among others, the potato, the oat, the large-fruited pineapple-strawberry of our gardens, the sour cherry, alfalfa, different varieties of grapes, raspberries, and blackberries, coffee and tea, dahlias, and numerous other species and varieties of ornamental plants. Autopolyploid forms having three homogeneous chromosome sets are the calamus, which is a cultivated plant that now grows wild, all the known cultivated varieties of bananas, and numerous valuable varieties of apples and pears.

The role of allopolyploidy in the origin of cultivated plants has been no less important. Thus, for instance, the plum *Prunus domestica,* with 48 chromosomes in its somatic cells, is an allopolyploid species to whose origin the blackthorn, *P. spinosa,* has contributed 32, and the cherry plum, *P.*

cerasifera, a native of the Middle East, 16 chromosomes. Common tobacco, *Nicotiana tabacum,* having 48 chromosomes, is a synthesized species derived from a cross between the wild species *N. sylvestris* and *N. tomentosa,* each of which has 24 chromosomes. Rape, *Brassica napus,* with its 38 chromosomes, has come into existence by the crossbreeding of species and subsequent duplication of chromosomes. Here, the parent species are the cabbage *B. oleracea,* with 18 chromosomes, and the turnip *B. campestris,* with 20 (Fig. 38).

The plant that most strikingly shows the important role

Fig. 38. Flowering plants of (*left*) turnip, (*right*) cabbage, and (*center*) their allopolyploid hybrid, rape. Note the marked heterosis (hybrid vigor) of the rape as compared to the parent species. (Redrawn after Olsson, from Müntzing)

of allopolyploidy in the origin of species and in the formation of numerous cultivated forms is wheat. In this genus there are species with 14 chromosomes, the so-called einkorn (one-grained) group. They include the one-grained wheat, or einkorn, *Triticum monococcum*, and its wild original form, *T. boeoticum*. The species of the second group, emmer, possess 28 chromosomes. This group contains the wild form, *T. dicoccoides;* macaroni wheat, *T. durum;* poulard, or rivet, wheat, *T. turgidum;* and a few other species. There are also wheats that have 42 chromosomes—the spelts. They include two species having fruits with glumes: spelt, *T. spelta,* and *T. macha,* and two naked-grain wheats, *T. aestivum,* common wheat, and Indian dwarf wheat, or shot wheat, *T. sphaerococcum.*

Summary of the hereditary relations of wheat, (*Triticum*) species (after E. Schiemann).

Wheat	Einkorn (one-grained) series, 14 chromosomes; chromosome set (Genom) AA	Emmer series, 28 chromosomes; chromosome set (Genom) AABB	Spelt series, 42 chromosomes; chromosome set (Genom) AABBDD
Wild form	Wild einkorn *T. boeoticum*	Wild emmer *T. dicoccoides* $\left(\begin{array}{c} T.\ Timopheevi \\ AAGG \end{array}\right)$	
Spelt	Cultivated einkorn *T. monococcum*	Emmer *T. dicoccum*	Spelt *T. spelta* *T. macha*
Naked-grained wheat		Macaroni wheat *T. durum* Poulard *T. turgidum* *T. orientale* *T. polonicum* *T. carthlicum*	Common wheat *T. aestivum* *T. sphaerococcum*

In wheat, too, the origin and relations of the individual groups of species can be explained by genetic experiments. The einkorn group possess a set of seven chromosomes that are contained in duplicate in every somatic cell and are designated as chromosome set A. Emmer, with 28 chromosomes, has two different sets of seven chromosomes each: the chromosome set A of the one-grained group plus a further set, B. Spelt, with its 42 chromosomes, carries a third set, D, in addition to the A and B sets.

On the basis of numerous genetic and cytologic studies, the following views about the origin of the three groups of wheat have been formed. From the hybridization of the wild einkorn form with another wild grass possessing chromosome set B—presumably either *Agropyron triticeum* or *Aegilops speltoides*—and a subsequent duplication of the chromosomes in the hybrid, the wild form of emmer originated, and from this the various species of the emmer series evolved by gene mutation and, partially, also by chromosome mutation. From hybridization of wild or cultivated emmer with a species of the grass genus *Aegilops,* which has the chromosome set D, and from subsequent polyploidy, the 42-chromosome spelt resulted.

This hypothesis has already been partly confirmed by experimental synthesis. American scientists have crossbred the wild form of emmer with *Aegilops squarrosa,* a wild species with 14 chromosomes having the D set, and have treated the hybrid plants of this crossing with colchicine in order to duplicate the chromosome set of the hybrid. In so doing, they succeeded in obtaining a fertile plant with 42 chromosomes containing in the A, B, and D sets in duplicate in its somatic cells. This new, synthetic wheat resembled spelt very closely and produced, when crossbred with it, fertile offspring. Thus, among the views on the origin of wheat species that have been outlined above, the one concerning spelt can be considered as confirmed.

While we know of wild species in both the einkorn and emmer series from which cultivated forms have arisen by gene mutation, such a wild original form does not exist for spelt. The results obtained by the experimental synthesis of spelt make this quite understandable. Here, by crossbreeding the wild form of emmer and a wild species of *Aegilops,* an allopolyploid new form originated that closely resembled an old cultivated plant, spelt. Thus, in this case a cultivated plant arose directly from the hybridization of two wild species. We may assume that the origin of spelt in prehistoric times took place in a similar fashion, and it is therefore not surprising that we know of no wild form in this series.

THE SUPERIORITY OF POLYPLOIDS AS CULTIVATED PLANTS

As a high-grade cultivated plant has arisen directly through allopolyploidy from two wild species, so in other cases the value of cultivated plants has been at least greatly increased by polyploidy. Common tobacco is a widespread cultivated plant, while its nonpolyploid original forms are semiwild species having no economic importance.

Oats and wheat illustrate clearly how much the value of cultivated plants can be increased by polyploidy. Among the oats, only the common oat, *Avena sativa,* is distributed all over the world as an important cultivated plant. Among wheat, the nonpolyploid einkorn is a primitive, low-yield cultivated form condemned to certain extinction and grown only in a few agriculturally underdeveloped regions. The species of the emmer series, with 28 chromosomes in their

Fig. 39. Ears of typical representatives of the three series of wheat: (*left to right*) common wheat (42 chromosomes); emmer (28 chromosomes); einkorn (14 chromosomes). (After Schwanitz)

somatic cells, show significantly higher variability and better adaptability and yield capacity, with the result that the species of this wheat group are widely distributed in Mediterranean areas and in other regions having similarly warm climates. The diversity of wheat forms culminates, however, in the 42-chromosome spelt, which has worldwide distribution in temperate zones and is among our most important cultivated plants (Fig. 39). [A similar increase in the number of chromosomes in strawberries leads to results shown in Fig. 40.]

The replacement of nonpolyploid forms by those of higher and higher degrees of polyploidy is shown most impressively in various ornamental plants. Until 1885 only nonpolyploid forms of the narcissus were known. At that time, the first varieties having three sets of chromosomes originated; these, owing to their larger flowers, quickly replaced the nonpoly-

Fig. 40. Species of strawberries of differing degrees of polyploidy that have played or still play a role as cultivated forms: (*left to right*) alpine strawberry, a cultivated form of the common wild strawberry, *Fragaria vesca* (14 chromosomes); Hautbor's strawberry, *F. moschata* (42 chromosomes); and the pineapple strawberry, *F. grandiflora* (56 chromosomes). Note the increase in the size of the fruit with the increasing degree of polyploidy.

ploid original forms, until they themselves were replaced around 1900 by still more splendid forms having four sets of chromosomes. Similar conditions exist in the garden hyacinth. In the garden iris, the replacement of nonpolyploid forms by polyploids was especially rapid. In Great Britain around 1915, only 33 percent of the hybrid varieties were polyploid; in 1920, 45 percent; in 1930, roughly 75 percent; and since 1940 the polyploids have been master in the field. In the garden larkspur, a wealth of excellent breeding varieties originated about the turn of the century with the appearance of the first allopolyploid hybrid species. Numerous other ornamental garden plants—such as the petunia, crocus, cyclamen, and primrose, to name just a few—include a large number of high-quality, large-flowered autopolyploid breeding varieties.

All these observations on individual species or genera have been confirmed by a study covering the thirty most important cultivated plants of worldwide economic importance. In this study, the world production of carbohydrates, fat, and protein was calculated separately for diploid and polyploid varieties. It was shown very clearly that polyploid cultivated plants are far superior to the nonpolyploids in the production of important foodstuffs.

REASONS FOR THE HIGHER YIELD CAPACITY OF POLYPLOIDS

Now we face the question of the actual reasons behind the obvious superiority of polyploid cultivated plants over nonpolyploid plants. First, it might well be the gigantism of the polyploids, which in many cases increases the value of a plant. It is certain, in the case of ornamental plants, that the increase in size and brilliance of flowers caused by polyploidy has been the decisive cause for the selection of and

preference for the polyploid forms (Fig. 41). The enlargement of fruits and seeds is another desirable result of polyploidy. In addition, duplication of chromosomes has in some
cases caused an increase in yield at the same time. Above
all, as seen before, the gigantism caused by polyploidy is
frequently accompanied by an improvement in crop quality.

More important than this direct effect of polyploidy—the
formation of gigas characters—is the multiplication of the
number of genes and the enlargement of yield capacity of
plants by polyploidy. By duplication or multiplication of
the chromosome sets in autopolyploids, the individual chromosomes, and hence all the genes located on them, are
multiplied accordingly. However, many genes have a quantitative effect, especially those genes on which the plant's
performance—its yield or quality—depends, which means
that the effects of individual genes add up. The more genes
present in a form that favorably influence the development

Fig. 41. Enlargement of the flower and increase in number of petals
(beginning of a trend toward formation of double flowers) resulting
from duplication of chromosomes in the cherry plum, *Prunus cerasifera: (left)* diploid flower, *(right)* tetraploid flower. (After Murawski and
Blasse)

of a plant, the more advantageous the development of the character they influence will be—that is, the better the yield capacity of the plant will be. The larger number of genes that is found in polyploids makes them able to achieve increases in performance that would never be possible in nonpolyploid plants.

Petunias provide an illustrative example of this. All the varieties of garden petunias that have the largest flowers are polyploid. The size of the flowers is apparently influenced by a gene that has a cumulative effect. The more genes there are in a plant that regulate large-flower size, the larger its flowers. Since many more large-flower genes can be combined in polyploid plants than in diploid ones, the polyploid plants can reach a flower size markedly exceeding that of the best diploid plants.

Furthermore, we see from many examples (Fig. 42, for instance) how much polyploidy can increase the variability of plants; marked variability is, however, as we have seen, a typical character of cultivated plants. Thus polyploidy supplies us with a large number of most different variants, and above all makes possible the much stronger development of all characters than could ever take place in diploid plants. Thus chances of finding particularly favorable and effective combinations through polyploidy are improving.

In modern plant breeding, heterosis, or hybrid vigor, plays a very important role, a phenomenon that takes place in the hybridization of hereditarily quite different varieties, races, or even species when the plants of the first hybrid generation surpass their parents in vigor of growth, number and size of flowers, fruits, and seeds, earliness of ripening, and other economically important characters (Fig. 43). In autopolyploids, heterosis can be much greater than in nonpolyploid plants, and it is probable that in plants that are propagated only vegetatively—such as potatoes, straw-

Fig. 42. Diversity of forms and wealth of colors in the garden dahlia *Dahlia variabilis* caused by high-degree polyploidy and hybridization of species: (*top row, left*) *Dahlia Merkii*, and (*right*) *D. coccinea*, two representatives of the two groups of 32-chromosome species whose hybridization gave rise to the wide diversity of varieties of 64-chromosome garden dahlias (*middle and bottom rows*).

berries, and most varieties of drupes—heterosis increased by polyploidy is an important cause of high yield capacity.

In allopolyploids, heterosis certainly plays a large role. As we have seen, allopolyploids are constant hybrids of different species that are too distantly related to one another

Fig. 43. Heterosis (hybrid vigor): (*left* and *center*) yield of two varieties of beans; (*right*) yield of the hybrid derived from their crossing. (After Quadt)

to be able to produce fertile hybrids when crossbred. This great difference, however, favors the development of hybrid vigor. On the other hand, the fact that allopolyploids are completely, or at least largely, genetically constant forms has the effect that heterosis in this instance is genetically fixed. And the combination of favorable genes of the different parent species may frequently be another essential cause of the high yield capacity of allopolyploid cultivated plants.

EXPERIMENTAL BREEDING OF POLYPLOIDS AND THE ECONOMIC IMPORTANCE OF THESE "NEW" POLYPLOIDS

In practical plant breeding, polyploid forms have appeared spontaneously again and again and have been selected especially by floriculturists for their larger and more variegated flowers and propagated as new breeding varieties without their being aware of special genetic peculiarities of these new large-flowered breeds. Occasionally, polyploids have also resulted from genetic experiments. Thus at the Royal Botanical Gardens at Kew, the new allotetraploid primrose species *Primula kewensis* originated through spontaneous duplication of the number of chromosomes of the completely sterile hybrid formed from the varieties *P. verticillata* and *P. floribunda*. Spontaneous duplication of the number of chromosomes in a sterile hybrid between wheat and rye resulted in the "Rimpau wheat-rye hybrid" in 1889 (Fig. 44).

When it was later established that numerous cultivated plants are polyploid, and when it was further believed that the excellent characters of many plants are due solely to polyploidy, repeated attempts were made to induce polyploidy artificially, especially by temperature shocks and chemicals, in order to obtain more efficient varieties of various cultivated plants. The result of all these efforts was not

Fig. 44. The allopolyploid Rimpau wheat-rye hybrid, *Triticale Rimpau,*
between its parent species: wheat (*Triticum aestivum*) and rye (*Secale
cereale*).

very satisfactory. Not until Blakeslee and Avery discovered the polyploidy-inducing effect of colchicine was a method found for making as many plants polyploid as one wants.

The great expectations of plant breeders for this new method of breeding were not fulfilled at first. The "new" polyploids did not prove to be more efficient in any way than their original diploid forms. As a rule, it turned out that the new polyploids could be used only as original material for further breeding efforts. As such, however, they offer breeders the opportunity to gain valuable new breeding varieties through hybridization and continued methodical selection. Although production of polyploids in plant breeding has been going on for only a rather short time, a number of successful achievements can be listed. In alfalfa and various species of clover, autopolyploid varieties giving up to 20 percent higher yields than their nonpolyploid original forms have been created. In red clover, moreover, the nutritional value of the polyploids has been increased, for they contain rather large amounts of an amino acid of which only traces are found in the nonpolyploid clovers and which is necessary in animal nutrition. A considerable increase in the yield of late turnips (Fig. 45), and especially of the sugar beet, can be achieved through polyploidy. In polyploid rye, whose yields at first were far below those of nonpolyploid varieties, it was possible to increase the productivity to such a degree that today we have polyploid varieties of rye that are equal or even superior to their nonpolyploid original forms. In the case of a number of ornamental garden plants, especially, there are polyploid varieties on the market that not only highly surpass nonpolyploid varieties in size and color intensity of flowers, but also equal them in liberal blossoming and number of flowers (Fig. 46, and see Fig. 3). [Further examples of increased yield due to polyploidy are shown for mint in Figs. 47 and 48, and for radishes in Fig. 49.]

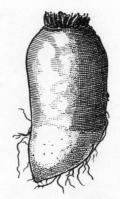

Fig. 45. (*Left*) Nonpolyploid late turnip, *Brassica campestris* var. *rapifera;* (*right*) root of the same variety, with duplicated number of chromosomes. (After Levan, from Müntzing)

Fig. 46. Improvement of polyploids by breeding: (*left*) one of the first polyploid varieties of the fairy primrose, *Primula malacoides,* introduced to Germany from the United States around 1928, showing the poverty of flowers that is characteristic of new polyploids; (*right*) present-day polyploid breeding form, showing an abundance of flowers. The photograph shows clearly how unfavorable characters that originally resulted from polyploidy can be eliminated altogether by carefully planned breeding. (After Böhnert and Mühlendyck)

Fig. 47. Higher yield in polyploid mint, *Mentha piperita:* (*left*) polyploid breeding stock; (*right*) plants of the nonpolyploid variety "Mitcham." (After G. Becker)

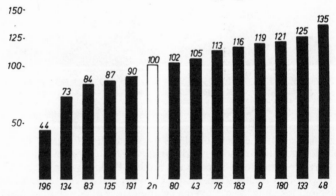

Fig. 48. Volatile-oil content (*black bars*) of various polyploid breeds of mint as percentages of that (*white bar*) of the nonpolyploid variety "Mitcham." (After G. Becker)

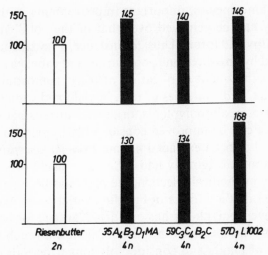

Fig. 49. (*Above*) Yield and (*below*) firmness of tubers in three polyploid races of radish (*Raphanus raphanistrum L.* var. *radicula* Pers.) as percentages of those of the nonpolyploid variety "Riesenbutter." (After G. Becker)

The production of allopolyploids has also become an important expedient in plant breeding. We need only recall here the numerous allopolyploid wheat-rye or wheat-Bermuda grass hybrids, which have become economically important as fodder plants. In the Loganberry and the Veitchberry we have two valuable new allopolyploids which are formed from the red raspberry and the blackberry, and from which some more valuable allopolyploid berries, such as the seedless and thornless Youngberry and Laxtonberry, have been derived. Favorable results may also be obtained by repeating the production of ancient allopolyploid cultivated plants. Original synthesis in these cases has occurred, as a rule, through the hybridization of wild species or of very primitive cultivated forms. It is obvious that, by a new synthesis of such allopolyploids from high-quality varieties of the same species, important improvements in the yield capacity can be achieved over that of the "old" allopolyploid cultivated forms. Thus, for instance, a "synthetic rape," obtained by crossbreeding good turnip and cabbage varieties and by subsequent duplication of the chromosomes, surpasses the "old" varieties of rape in yield and winter hardiness. Also, in allopolyploids, originally unsatisfactory performance can be improved considerably by selection being continued over an extended period. *Primula kewensis,* mentioned above, originally had little value as an ornamental plant; by methodical selection, the plant has been so greatly improved that a number of breeding varieties are available.

However, polyploidy has one disadvantage for breeders. Owing to the increased number of genes, a much greater number of plants and considerably longer periods of time are needed to obtain the desired combination of favorable genes and the high yields that result. But this disadvantage is more than compensated for in the polyploids because, by means of continued selection, performances can be achieved that nonpolyploid plants could never be capable of. This possibility of combining a large number of favorable genes in one plant may well have been, as mentioned earlier, the cause of the superiority of polyploids over the diploid gigas plants.

FURTHER MUTATIONAL PROCESSES THAT MAY PLAY A ROLE IN THE ORIGIN OF CULTIVATED-PLANT CHARACTERS

As all organisms are subject to genetic changes, so polyploid plants cannot forever maintain the characters they possessed at the time of their origin. Gene mutations and changes in the structure of chromosomes occur in them, too, but a special role is played by aneuploidy: the loss or multiplication of single chromosomes or pairs of chromosomes. It has been found that various important cultivated plants are such aneuploids. In this connection, drupes—apples, pears, and quinces—should be mentioned in particular. They all have 17 chromosomes in their germ cells. Study of the behavior of chromosomes during the development of the germ cells has shown, however, that the original number of chromosomes in these species was seven. Of these seven chromosomes, three were tripled and the others doubled. Wheat and rice are also aneuploid plants, with a basic chromosome number of five, not seven or twelve. In cabbage, which has nine chromosomes in its germ cells, the actual number is six, for three chromosomes exist in duplicate. Flax originated from a still-unknown species through the loss of one chromosome.

All of these aneuploids are cultivated plants that play an important economic role. We do not know of either polyploid or nonpolyploid original forms of any of them. Hence we have to assume that these aneuploids were more successful in the struggle for life and better suited for the origin of cultivated plants than their original species with complete sets of chromosomes. Valuable aneuploid varieties are known among cultivated plants in sugar cane, bananas, hyacinths, and Kentucky bluegrass.

Finally, the genetic factors located in the plasma might be credited with having some influence on the characters and performance of cultivated plants. Thus it could be shown that characters affecting the yield of plants are determined by plasmatic factors, and also that heterosis, or hybrid vigor, is evidently partially determined by the genetic individuality of the plasma. Hence in surveying the genetic forces that have caused the origin of cultivated plants, the genetic factors located in the plasma should be taken into consideration.

CHAPTER 3

The Influence of Environment on the Origin of Cultivated Plants

NATURAL AND ARTIFICIAL SELECTION

The cultivated plant is the product of plant breeding. In accordance with a statement by the well-known Russian botanist Vavilov, we may regard this as interference by man with the origin of plant forms, that is, as a partial process of phylogenetic history that is directed by the will of man. As the hereditary constitution of plants in nature is subject to steady alteration and as new varieties and species constantly originate, so, too, the plant alters under human custody. Cultivated forms arise from wild species. These change, their diversity increases, their performance improves and becomes more diversified, and thus they depart more and more from their wild original forms until, finally, totally new plants exist whose origin may in some cases be quite difficult to determine.

Both processes—the origin of species in nature and the selective transformation of wild forms into actual cultivated plants—are based on the same biological processes: the production of a wide diversity of forms by various mutational processes and, on the other hand, reduction of this diversity by selection.

The first of these two forces, the ability to "mutate," is the basis both of phylogenetic evolution in nature and of the origin of new and improved forms through plant breeding. The difference between natural selection and artificial selection governed by man is due solely to different kinds of selection. Selection in nature results in the survival of only those new mutants that meet the requirements imposed on them by climatic conditions, soil, and natural competition for space and food. The result of this process of selection is the adaptation of plants to the conditions of a given natural environment.

Cultivated plants are also exposed to the influences of their environment; they too are threatened by frost and drought, pests and disease. But man has been careful to protect the plants that are useful to him from excessive hazard. By tilling and fertilizing the soil, by regulating the water supply and eliminating the struggle for life, and by protecting plants from pests and disease, he has created an artificial environment that favors the plant more and, above all, exposes it to less rigorous requirements than those met in nature. Hence natural selection in cultivated forms is less harsh than that among wild plants.

To the mitigation of the struggle for life, man has added another effective force, artificial selection, whose importance for the origin of cultivated plants was recognized by Charles Darwin. While through natural selection only vital organisms that are fit to meet the "struggle for existence" are able to survive and reproduce, man, by means of artificial selection, ensures that the valuable characters of plants useful to him are strengthened and improved. Thus he intensifies all the characters that make the plant seem valuable to him (Fig. 50). On the other hand, the structure and developmental rhythm of the plant are also altered in such a way as to make it particularly adapted to cultivation. In this way, the value of the plant for man is increased, but for survival in the struggle for existence in nature most of these properties are detrimental. Hence cultivated plants as a rule are no longer capable of surviving and propagating without constant help from man. The loss of natural means of pro-

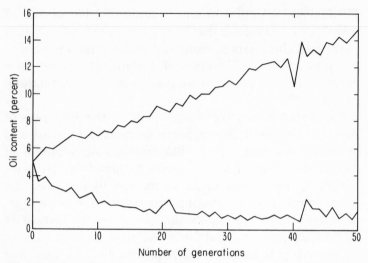

Fig. 50. The effect of continuous selection over fifty generations of maize according to high or low oil content. (After Woodworth and others, from Hayes, Immer, and Smith)

tection and of dissemination, which characterizes cultivated plants, has this effect. But numerous other characters that are typical of cultivated plants, such as the tenderness of leaves and the formation of fleshy roots in many salad and vegetable plants, or the formation of heads in cabbage and lettuce, make the plant unfit for survival without human care and protection.

Though cultivated plants are "domesticated" plants, being the products of artificial selection and having lost many of the characters that enabled their wild-growing original forms to survive the struggle for existence in woods and fields, they are nevertheless not completely independent of the influence of environment. Man certainly tries to provide for them an environment in which they can develop their favorable properties as far as possible. Nevertheless, this cannot prevent their remaining under the influence of climate and soil conditions. These factors cause rigorous selection among cultivated plants, too. Therefore, only such varieties survive as are really able to meet the climatic and soil conditions of a region. Varieties deriving from dry regions thus are largely drought-resistant; cultivated plants from regions having severe winters possess strong resistance to frost; varieties from sandy soils are marked by great insensitivity.

A particularly illustrative example of the adaptation of cultivated plants to their environment is provided by the photoperiodic behavior of plants. As is generally known, the day during the main vegetation period in the temperate zones is much longer than it is in the tropics. Many plants, including a number of cultivated ones, are so well adapted to the length of day that prevails in their native region that they will produce flowers and fruits only under the same conditions. Useful plants from the tropics are frequently short-day plants; that is, they can reach the blooming stage quickly or develop flower buds only when the days are short. Plants from more northerly or southerly latitudes, on the other hand, are long-day plants, needing a longer day in order to complete their developmental cycle quickly. Plants grown in hothouses come mostly from the tropics; this is the reason why many of them bloom during the winter, when the days are short.

This photoperiodism can considerably hamper the introduction of cultivated plants into regions having different lengths of day. The high economic value of the soybean has led to numerous attempts from the middle of the last century onward to introduce and acclimatize this plant in central Europe. These efforts failed for a long time because all imported varieties were short-day plants. They grew overabundantly and produced huge foliage, but reached blooming and fruiting too late to yield satisfactory amounts of fruits and seeds with certainty. Only after a day-neutral variety had been discovered in northern Manchuria—a variety in which blooming is not influenced by length of day—could soybeans be successfully cultivated and bred in Europe and North America.

High-yield varieties of cultivated plants are, after all, a product of given environmental conditions. They differ from the primitive and inferior native varieties, from which they originated mainly by a capacity to exploit especially well larger amounts of nutritional substances in the soil. Highbred varieties react to increased application of manure with essentially higher increases of yield than primitive indigenous varieties do, and hence are extraordinarily well adapted to high nutritional content of soil. This special qualification of highbred varieties for cultivation in fertile soil is the result of a particular selection process. The breeding of cultivated plants has been carried on since the middle of the nineteenth century in experimental gardens, field parcels with particularly well and carefully tilled and richly fertilized soils. Plants find extremely favorable conditions for growth and food requirements in these experimental gardens, and since they also have significantly more growing space there than in a regular field, they can develop their inherent properties to the fullest extent. Plants having the ability to respond to good feeding with high yields must, under the favorable conditions of the test field, exhibit their high hereditary yield capacity. By continued selection of particularly efficient plants from the rich soils of the experimental gardens, intensive varieties have been created, which are superior to the old field varieties if they are grown in well-manured and cultivated soil. In poor, badly manured soil, however, they can barely cope with extensive varieties and sometimes even fall behind them.

"PRIMARY" AND "SECONDARY" CULTIVATED PLANTS

The first useful plants that were methodically grown by man derived directly from gathered plants. The observation that, in the rich soil around human dwellings, gathered plants germinated by chance from lost seeds, developed particularly luxuriantly, and gave unusually high yields may have induced the first methodical cultivation of such useful plants. Consequently, this became the cause for the gradual transformation of wild forms into actual cultivated plants. These plants, which were taken under cultivation directly because of their favorable characters, are called "primary" cultivated plants. All of them have high nutritive requirements, belonging ecologically to the group of ruderal plants, that is, to those plant communities that usually grow among rubbish and in similar places having very rich soil. These "primary" cultivated plants include most varieties of wheat, barley, various millets, rice, maize, sugar cane, tobacco, flax, soybeans, rape, and cotton.

Quite close to these primary cultivated plants is another group, which are considered "secondary" cultivated plants mainly because of the fact that they became cultivated plants later on. They are the so-called "anthropochorous" plants, species that also like highly nutritious soil, especially soil having high nitrogen content. They tend to gather in the immediate vicinity of human dwellings, since they find favorable conditions for existence there. These plants include hemp, poppies, cabbage, mangel-wurzel, forage and sugar beets, and various medicinal plants.

A plant that has become a regular companion to man and is used as a gathered plant without having turned into a cultivated plant is the European elder, *Sambucus nigra*. Similarly, the stinging nettle, *Urtica dioica*, belongs among these;

it is an anthropochorous plant that is still a wild form. In times of need, however, it has been gathered again and again not only for eating, as a kind of spinach, but also for its fibers, and occasionally it has even been used by breeders.

The example of another plant in this group shows very clearly how the cultivation of such an anthropochorous plant may have arisen. The alpine sorrel, *Rumex alpinus,* is an old gathered plant of the Alps. It used to be a popular vegetable, but nowadays is merely a forage plant. Alpine sorrel has not only been gathered by peasants in the vicinity of alpine huts, where it occurs in large quantities owing to the richness of the soil, but has also occasionally been fenced in, and perhaps even cultivated a little. On migrations to other regions, it was taken along and sown in places where it had not previously existed. Since only such plants as were particularly large and beautiful even at this preagricultural stage were allowed to form seeds, an improvement of the wild plant by methodical selection took place.

The group of cultivated plants that has arisen from anthropochorous plants requires at least the same nutritive richness of the soil that the "primary" cultivated plants do. Further significant characteristics are the lack of native habitat of these cultivated plants—resulting from their close dependence upon man and his environment—and the fact that some of these species have been taken under cultivation simultaneously in different regions or at very different times.

A group of particular interest are the "secondary" cultivated plants, which have acquired their cultivated-plant characters as weeds among cultivated plants. The transformation of the plant from a wild species to a weed and to a cultivated plant occurs because of the particular environmental conditions that are created by man in growing certain cultivated plants. In the cultivation of various species of useful plants, differing conditions prevail. In a rye field, conditions are totally different from those in a stand of maize, and these in turn differ greatly from the ecologic conditions prevailing in a field of clover or potatoes. A weed species can maintain its existence only if its life rhythm, development, and numerous other qualities are well adapted to the specific characters of the cultivated plant with which it is associated. This is especially true with respect to the size of fruits and seeds. Here we can also recognize the causes that have led to an increase in the size of these organs in a number of weed species. Man learned quite early to sift grain and other large seeds by winnowing, that is, by throwing the seeds against the wind with a shovel. The heavy fruits and seeds of the cultivated plants were thrown much farther than the light chaff and weed seeds. By this method, all those hereditary variants of weed species that came close in size and weight of seeds to their host species attained a positive selection value. Thus, unintentionally and unconsciously, man selected for large-seededness and hence, most probably, for gigantism at the same time, the weeds of all cultivated plants whose seeds were sifted by winnowing. Quite similarly, only such wild grasses as had a similar developmental rhythm and ripened at the same time as cereals could survive as weeds among them. Among cultivated cereals possessing rigid rachises, the associated weeds had to lose their capacity for free dissemination and acquire rigid rachises, since only then could they be threshed out with the cereals and get in with the seed grain for the following year.

Thus in a number of weeds, mutations causing certain characters of cultivated plants have gained a positive selective value, and mutations that, in an ordinary wild species, would have decreased if not destroyed the species' chances for survival, have caused in these weeds an increase of adaptability to the cultivation environment they have chosen. In this way, certain weeds over the course of time have attained more and more cultivated-plant characters, finally being taken under cultivation for their newly acquired valuable qualities.

Particularly illustrative of the changes undergone by weeds in association with certain cultivated plants is the example of flax weeds. Some of them have assimilated their external features to those of flax to such a degree that, at first glance, they may be mistaken for flax, and hence are not conspicuous in a flax field. All of these weeds exhibit great similarity both to flax and to each other, since analogous selective conditions have caused, in very different species, analogous growth patterns. All these weeds differ so widely from their wild original species that they are considered species in their own right. Adaptation to the host plant goes so far in these flax weeds that there are a number of races that differ from each other, but show a closer resemblance to a variety of flax, namely, that variety among which they are growing as weeds (Fig 51). The exceedingly great dependence of the origin of cultivated-plant characters in flax weeds on the conditions of cultivation becomes clear in comparing the weeds of regions having primitive agriculture with those in a more highly developed one. It is clearly shown that the more progressive the agriculture the more nearly perfect the adaptation of the weeds to the flax, and hence the more strongly developed their cultivated-plant characters. And the better the method of sifting the seed grain, the less possible it is for any other weed seeds to get through except those that resemble flax in all essential seed or fruit characters. Adaptation of flax weeds to the various cultivated forms of flax is so extensive that, on the basis of a precise investigation of the present-day geographic dis-

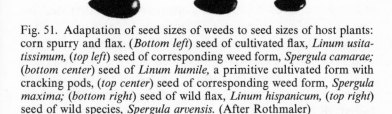

Fig. 51. Adaptation of seed sizes of weeds to seed sizes of host plants: corn spurry and flax. (*Bottom left*) seed of cultivated flax, *Linum usitatissimum*, (*top left*) seed of corresponding weed form, *Spergula camarae;* (*bottom center*) seed of *Linum humile,* a primitive cultivated form with cracking pods, (*top center*) seed of corresponding weed form, *Spergula maxima;* (*bottom right*) seed of wild flax, *Linum hispanicum,* (*top right*) seed of wild species, *Spergula arvensis.* (After Rothmaler)

tribution of the various weed species and races, conclusions about the native habitat and routes of dispersion of the individual forms of flax can be drawn.

We have seen that weed species can also adapt seed size to that of the cultivated species with which they are associated. In so doing, the seeds or fruitlets of the weeds increase their size, as a rule. However, this is not always the case, especially with some flax weeds of the grass genus *Lolium* (rye grass), whose fruitlets have become smaller than they were in the original forms by assimilating to the seed size of the respective varieties of flax. With the reduced size of the fruitlets, the whole plant has become smaller and more delicate than the original species, so that these original species, compared with their derived species, give the impression of being giant forms. In this example, too, the frequently mentioned relation between seed size and growth is clearly recognizable.

From flax weeds various species have evolved into actual cultivated plants, such as gold-of-pleasure (*Camelina sativa* and *C. linicola*), corn spurry (*Spergula maxima* and *S.*

linicola), white mustard (*Sinapis alba*), rocket (*Eruca sativa*), and turnip (*Brassica campestris*). Other cultivated plants originating from weeds are rye, various cultivated oats, vetches, peas, beans, and varieties of spring vetch.

Rye, *Secale cereale,* is still widely distributed as a weed in the wheat and barley fields of the Middle East, where it has become an annual and attained such other decisive cultivated-plant characters as large-seededness and rigidity of rachis. Rye as a weed followed the dispersion of wheat, and through this association evolved into a cultivated plant of its own. With the penetration into more severe climatic zones and poorer soils the demanding and sensitive wheat failed. Rye, on the other hand, as with all weeds and all cultivated plants originating from weeds, had very modest requirements, still fit for poorer conditions. Thus the less favorable conditions were for the cultivation of wheat, the more rye put itself forward. This process can still be observed today in Anatolia, where rye, as mentioned above, occurs as a weed in wheat fields. Wherever conditions there are unfavorable for wheat, rye develops richly. Owing to inefficient sifting of seed material the portion of rye in the composition of the crop and in the seed harvest increases from year to year until such time as seeds for sowing are carefully selected by hand, whereupon the cycle starts over again. This development has evidently taken place whenever wheat invaded regions whether in the mountains or on the northward migration—where conditions became less favorable for it. Where wheat has failed to thrive, rye has gained importance because of its hardiness and resistance; in such regions, it has equaled or even exceeded wheat in economic importance, and has finally evolved into an independent cultivated plant claiming and occupying not inconsiderable cultivated areas of its own.

In other species too, especially in the Middle East, the

transition from wild species through weeds to cultivated plants can be followed clearly. Wild, or, better, "weed," peas, *Pisum elatius,* as well as "wild beans," *Vicia narbonensis,* are not disliked by peasants, even as weeds among their grain fields, since, after severe winters when the wheat has been damaged by frost, or after dry springs, when the barley has germinated poorly on account of the drought, they develop abundantly and form, together with the remaining grain, dense stands yielding good harvests of a mixture of grain, peas, and beans, which is used, after being crushed, for forage, and, after being ground, for bread flour. Other herbaceous Leguminosae, such as the camel thorn, *Alhagi camelorum,* or *Prosopis stephaniana,* are similarly welcome as weeds, since they yield cattle fodder after the grain has been harvested and also improve the fertility of the soil. Out of the toleration, or even the furtherance, of those weeds that had already attained some characters of cultivated plants may have originated the custom of mixed cultivation, an ancient custom in Asia. This again was the starting point for the actual cultivation of secondary cultivated plants.

The origin of cultivated characters in weeds is by no means restricted to the weeds of primary cultivated plants. Once a cultivated plant has evolved from a weed species, the same conditions of selection exist in its cultivation as in that of primary cultivated plants, and the weeds growing among secondary cultivated plants have to adopt cultivated-plant characters for the same reasons that are valid in the case of weeds of primary cultivated plants. Thus two grass species occurring among rye, chess grass, *Bromus secalinus,* and the related species *B. grossus,* have acquired large fruitlets and rigid rachises, though they have not yet attained the status of actual cultivated plants. Corncockle, *Agrostemma githago,* has also, as a rye weed, adopted many valuable properties, such as large seeds and almost complete closing of the fruit capsules, so that, before World War I, a race having particularly large seeds was cultivated in Russia as raw material for producing alcohol. A variety of sand oat, *Avena strigosa* subvar. *uniflora*, has adapted its grain size to that of rye, among which it grows as a weed. Other varieties of the same species have achieved cultivated-plant characters through growing as weeds among the oat *Avena fatua* ssp. *sativa*, which itself evolved from the wild oat (*Avena fatua* ssp. *fatua*), a weed growing among emmer and barley that was grown as a cultivated plant in the poor soil of northwest Europe.

THE NATIVE HABITATS OF CULTIVATED PLANTS

Most of our cultivated plants have vast areas of distribution, many of them being cosmopolites that can be found on all continents. This worldwide distribution of numerous cultivated plants stems from the fact that man carried his cultivated plants with him on his migrations, thus introducing them into new areas. Commerce has also promoted the dispersal of valuable cultivated plants since early times, and the opening of the world through modern trade has contributed to the growth of economically important cultivated plants the world over, wherever climatic conditions and soil permit their cultivation. With cultivated plants, weeds disperse, and anthropochorous plants also find suitable living conditions around human dwellings everywhere, so that they have become the inseparable companions of man even far beyond the borders of their regions of origin.

Migrations of cultivated plants in many cases began as long ago as the early period of human history. It has therefore not always been easy to determine the origin and native habitat of individual cultivated plants, especially since the wild species from which they came were unknown for a long time. Under these circumstances, it is understandable that "homelessness" was long considered a typical characteristic of many cultivated and anthropochorous plants and weeds. With the extension and deepening of our knowledge of cultivated plants, these assumptions have come to be recognized more and more as being erroneous. More than anyone else, Vavilov and his co-workers can be credited with broadening our ideas about the native habitats of cultivated plants. With a tremendous amount of material assembled on numerous collecting trips all over the world, Vavilov examined the geographic distribution of the subspecies, varieties, and all the hereditary variants in our most important cultivated plants. He found that the wealth of existing forms is not at all evenly distributed over the entire area occupied by cultivated plants concerned, but that certain regions exist where a particularly rich abundance of heterogeneous forms can be found, while outside these regions the diversity of forms is much less. Vavilov calls these regions having the greatest wealth of forms gene or diversity centers. Today, we distinguish eight different gene centers, each a center of diversity for a large number of various cultivated plants, and all distinguished by a common character: all of them are situated in the mountains of the subtropics or the tropics (Fig. 52).

The kind and distribution of hereditary variants within gene centers was investigated. At times diversity proved to be greatest in the middle of the gene centers, decreasing toward border areas. It further appeared that in the hearts of the gene centers dominant alleles of the various genes prevailed, and that toward the peripheral regions these were replaced increasingly by recessive alleles. From crosses between wild species and cultivated plants derived from them,

Fig. 52. The gene centers of the world. (After Vavilov)

1. Southwest Asia: naked millet, naked oat, hexastichous bearded and naked barley, soybean, China and Peking cabbage, radish, tea, peach, apricot, orange, lemon.

2. India and Indochina, including the Malay Peninsula: rice, sugar cane, Indian cotton, coconut palm, banana, numerous tropical fruits.

3. Central Asia: common wheat (secondary center) and Indian dwarf wheat, pea, lentil, garden bean, radish, spinach, onion, garlic, almond, pear, apple.

4. Middle East: einkorn, common wheat, distichous barley, rye, Mediterranean oat, flax, alfalfa, morello cherry, plum, carrot.

5. Mediterranean region: emmer, bearded wheat, large-grained forms of barley, pea, lentil, garden bean, flax, mangel-wurzel, numerous vegetables and forage plants.

6. Ethiopia: secondary center for emmer, bearded wheat, barley, millets, Arabian coffee.

7. Southern Mexico and Central America: maize (secondary center), various species of beans and pumpkins, New World cotton, sisal, red pepper, *rustica* tobacco, cacao tree.

8. South America: maize, tomato, pumpkin, potato, common tobacco, cotton, peanut, pineapple.

we know that wild-plant characters are, as a rule, inherited by dominant alleles, while the corresponding characters of cultivated plants are inherited by recessive alleles of the same genes. The accumulation of dominant alleles in the core regions of gene centers was interpreted by Vavilov as indicating that the original progenitors of the cultivated plants in question are located there. Through mutation, new recessive types constantly arise that are partially suppressed by hybridization or, being unfit to cope with the conditions that prevail in these regions, are rapidly eliminated through selection. With increasing distance from the middle of the gene center, ecologic conditions, and hence conditions of selection, change. Thus mutants that differ physiologically from the original form can survive competition or even be furthered. And so the dominant alleles from the heart of the gene center are replaced by recessive alleles.

Accordingly, the process of development of cultivated forms from their wild original species would have occurred within the gene centers and, according to Vavilov, would essentially be an evolutionary process consisting of the loss of dominant alleles and their replacement by recessive ones. Thus Vavilov considers these gene centers both as the regions of origin and as sources of dispersal for the cultivated plants that develop a great wealth of hereditary variants there. Today, we have to distinguish between primary and secondary, or accumulation, centers. In the primary gene centers, the cultivated plants in question evolved from wild forms native to this region. As cultivated plants, they entered another gene center at some time, and the same natural forces that caused the origin of the great diversity of forms in the primary gene center again cause a considerable increase in diversity of the cultivated plant that came to this region. In this way, a new, or "secondary," gene center develops for the cultivated plant in question.

Thus the center of origin of spelt seems to be the gene center in the Middle East. Here, the parent species, wild and cultivated emmer, as well as *Aegilops squarrosa*, occurred together and were easily capable of producing spelt by hybridization and spontaneous duplication of numbers of chromosomes in the hybrid. Proceeding from this region, spelt reached, in its eastward migration, the central Asian gene center, where it formed a large number of new varieties. Ethiopia must be considered the secondary gene center for emmer and barley. The Mediterranean region has become the secondary gene center for a whole series of species characterized especially by the peculiarity that a number of cultivated plants that have small seeds in other gene centers, such as peas, lentils, flax, and barley, occur there in large-seeded varieties. Today, a number of smaller regions have become known that may be considered secondary gene centers. These include, for instance, the northern border of the Alpine region, which is considered the secondary gene center for spelt.

It is a very singular fact that the origin of our most important cultivated plants is evidently restricted to a few limited regions of the globe. Moreover, these exhibit a very peculiar correspondence to one another: all of them are located in mountainous regions of the hot or warm zones of the Old and the New World. Under these circumstances, the assumption that the climatic conditions of these regions are the cause of the origin of the wealth of diversity seems warranted.

It is assumed, first, that the exceedingly wide temperature fluctuations of the mountains of the subtropics and the tropics can increase the rate of mutation both in the germinating seed and in the growing plant. To this may be added the mutations induced by strong ultraviolet radiation, which could especially easily affect pollen grains. In tropical mountains, new mutants find vastly differing conditions side by side. Experimental investigations have shown repeatedly that mutants that are less viable and efficient than the normal form under environmental conditions usual to the species may be far superior under changed circumstances. The extraordinary diversity of microclimate that is characteristic of all mountains, especially tropical ones, makes it easier for the newly originated mutants to find a suitable environment than it would be in a region with a uniform, balanced climate. Hence in these tropical and subtropical climates many mutants, in particular, have survived. The fact that, in this way, a large number of highly differing alleles of numerous genes occur in the gene centers in a highly limited area promotes the combination of favorable alleles in the plant through hybridization. Even this seems to be furthered favorably by the climatic conditions prevailing in the gene centers, for, according to observations made by the German Hindu Kush expedition, species of cereals that are strictly self-fertilizing in European countries exhibit a tendency toward cross-fertilization there. To maintain the great diversity in the gene centers, it is important that the agriculture in the mountains, in which most of these centers are located, be at a very primitive stage of development. Every peasant grows his own seed for the next sowing. This means that every mutation occurring in these regions in the field has a much greater chance of preservation than it would in regions having progressive agriculture, where practically all seed used for sowing is bought from a very few specialized breeding stations. Furthermore, the selection of seed produced is much poorer. Hence new mutants are not eliminated at once, as is usually the case in countries having highly developed agriculture. Instead, they have a much better chance of being preserved over long periods, provided they are not unfit for survival.

These features of the gene centers probably led to the origin and preservation of a rather great diversity of forms among wild plants. Hence the occurrence of favorable mutants must also have been furthered there and, since increased natural hybridization also favors the combination of advantageous traits, it becomes understandable that such a great number of cultivated plants have evolved from wild species just in these regions. The newly evolved cultivated plants, however, are exposed to the same external conditions as the wild species, and so a wide diversity of forms must develop among them as well.

When the cultivated plant moves out of the region of the gene center with man's help, it comes under environmental influences that do not correspond at all to those of its region of origin. Supposedly, the rate of mutation will diminish under the essentially less extreme external conditions, whereas environmental factors become much more homogeneous over larger areas. These areas, which the cultivated plant now has to pass in its migration, function as sieves, so to speak, holding back from the original abundance of forms now many, now few, of the carriers of all those characters that are unfavorable to the plant's thriving in this climatic region or in a certain soil. The farther a cultivated plant strays from its region of origin, the more different sieves it has to pass and the narrower its original diversity of forms necessarily becomes.

This development may change, however, as soon as man introduces the plant into another gene center. Here again, external conditions that favor the origin of a great diversity of forms influence it. In this way, a new secondary gene center comes into being for the species. If the environmental factors, and hence the selective conditions, differ essentially here from those in the primary gene center, it is possible that in the secondary center new characters will appear in the species. The Mediterranean region offers an example of this. There the climatic conditions seem to favor the origin of gigas forms with particularly large seeds of numerous cultivated plants that occur in Asia only in small-seeded and small-fruited varieties: peas, lentils, beans, flax, and barley.

Modern agriculture, and especially plant breeding, with its efforts to develop a limited number of thoroughly homogeneous breeding varieties, have led to a marked impoverishment of the diversity of forms in our intensively bred cultivated plants. This development has repeatedly proved to be quite unfavorable and hampering, particularly when the breeding of qualities that cultivated plants did not previously possess was at stake, such as resistance to disease or increased winter hardiness. Since a large number of very diverse hereditary variants can be found in the gene centers, they have become important rich sources for plant breeders, who started after World War I to exploit them on numerous collecting trips.

ON THE "DEGENERATION" OF CULTIVATED PLANTS

Artificial selection by man has caused cultivated plants to adopt a number of characters that make them particularly valuable to him, but it is these same cultivated plant characters that make it impossible for the plant to survive and propagate without constant care.

In this connection, only the "root" formation in cultivated carrots, kohlrabi, and turnips need be recalled. These savory, fleshy organs expose the plants to increased damage from animal enemies. In addition, these tender formations, in contrast to the tough roots of the wild forms, fail to be frost-resistant because of their high water content. Since the growth of fleshy roots seems as a rule to be connected with the fact that the plants do not bloom and fruit before their second year, the carriers of these "deformities" would perish, without human care, before they could reproduce. If we were to apply to cultivated plants the same standards we use for measuring the vitality and performance of wild species, we doubtless would have to call all of them "degenerate" and consider most of their typical cultivated-plant characters as "pathological" and "anomalous" formations. Cultivated plants are, as it were, carriers of "hereditary diseases" that increase their value for man.

However, not all of the changes signify real improvements as far as man is concerned. Ignorant of actual biological value, man has occasionally created breeding varieties that must be regarded as inferior from the point of view of quality. Among these belong all vegetable varieties having yellowish leaves, as well as wax beans, and head cabbages that have white instead of yellowish leaves at the heart of the head. None of these forms are in any way "tenderer" or better tasting, and they are essentially poorer in vitamins than the normal green varieties. The heavy curling of leaves characteristic of many varieties of kale must be regarded as a similar sort of "misbreeding." With the increase in curling, the leaves become coarser, harder, and less digestible. Thus selection for improvement of a character that appeals only to the eye of the gardener and the housewife—when the kale is ready for the table the degree of curling is hardly noticeable—has led to a decrease in quality.

Another consequence of wrong selection is the familiar "bursting" of carnations (Fig. 53), which is now so common among the Chabaud strains and other carnations that gardeners cannot prevent this malformation, which makes the flowers unfit to sell, unless they put a thin wire around the calyx. The bursting of the flowers is caused by breeders' trying to attain an excessively rich doubling of the flowers. These endeavors have been successful: the number of petals has been increasingly augmented, and has finally become so large that, during the unfolding of the flower, the calyx

Fig. 53. "Burst" flower of a carnation next to an unburst flower of the same variety.

often can no longer stand the pressure of the growing petals and splits on one side. This is especially likely to happen when the flower bud is globular or has its largest diameter at its base. By overdoing or choosing wrong goals of selection in some instances, man has thus created cultivated forms that must be called "degenerate" despite their usefulness to man.

"The exploitation of the anomalous and the pathological" in plant breeding culminates in desirable properties being caused by contagious diseases. One such instance has gained importance even in the history of human civilization. In the early seventeenth century in Holland there developed a fondness for tulips, especially among the upper class. This vogue turned into a tulip craze that came to be known by the name "tulipomania," when tulips with two-colored, striped flowers appeared. Up to 13,000 Dutch guilders were paid for a viable bulb of the most famous of these new varieties, the "Semper Augustus." We now know that the mottling of the petals—found even today in some varieties of tulips (Fig. 54)—is the consequence of a virus infection. Since tulip varieties are propagated by bulbs, and since disease is passed on from mother to daughter bulbs, only forms with mottled petals appear in the offspring of an infected plant, which gives the impression that this character is an actual hereditary character of this breed.

Also because of a virus infection green-white mottling is carried over in a variety called *Abutilon thompsoni* of the species *Abutilon striatum,* which belongs to the Malvaceae. White mottling of leaves, an anomaly popular with gardeners and gardening enthusiasts, also occurs frequently in

Fig. 54. Flower of a modern virus-infected tulip variety.

other plants and normally is caused by a certain genetic constitution, which in this case is the symptom of a disease.

Thus while we can refer to all cultivated plants in general as being degenerate in respect to their ability to live and survive in nature, we commonly understand "degeneration" in cultivated plants to be a completely different process—in fact, quite the opposite process to the phenomenon just mentioned—namely, highbred varieties can slacken in their performance unless the breeder keeps them to the standard they have achieved through stabilizing selection and continuous selection of the best individual plants.

Such loss of typically valuable qualities through slackening or discontinuance of care on the part of the breeder is due to the fact that performance of cultivated plants is based on a large number of genes. Thus with maize, the number of genes upon which the yield is based is estimated to be at least 200, the protein content is determined by at least 22, and the oil content by more than 20. It is understandable that, particularly with cross fertilization, it is scarcely possible to bring together the favorable alleles of all these numerous genes having to do with performance and yield in one plant, let alone in one breeding variety, in homozygous form; these will always be more or less heterozygous. But this has the effect that they "segregate" in their performance and hence tend to diminish in performance from generation to generation unless man takes care to preserve the original level of performance by stabilizing selection.

This slackening of performance is especially striking among the offspring of plants that exhibit heterosis. By heterosis or hybrid vigor we mean the phenomenon whereby hybrids of certain breeding varieties, races, or species show greater vigor, faster development, and better yield than either of their parent species. Today, this "luxuri-

ance of hybrids" is explained mainly by the marked heterozygosis or dissimilarity of the hybrids. The combination of
various alleles of the same genes in one plant seems to be
sufficient to cause heterosis. In other cases, heterosis is
obviously due to the combination in the hybrid of favorable
alleles of different genes from both parents, so that it possesses favorable alleles of many more genes than does either
of its parents. If these alleles for increased performance are
dominant, the hybrid, with its larger number of dominant
alleles, must consequently be superior to its parents. But
since it is heterozygous in a number of these genes, there
must occur among its offspring segregation of these valuable
qualities. With the correlated decrease of heterozygosis and
of the number of dominant alleles, the production of organic
substances by them must also decrease from generation to
generation. Hence varieties exhibiting heterosis have to be
constantly re-created by breeders, for left to themselves they
deteriorate quickly.

Our fruit and potato varieties and many garden flowers
are strongly heterozygous combinations of particularly
favorable alleles. As a matter of fact, all these varieties are
merely individual organisms with remarkable performances
owing to an especially favorable combination of genes.
These unique combinations of genes are preserved and
propagated vegetatively by means of bulbs, runners, cuttings,
and grafts. If offspring are raised from seed of such a clone,
new plants result from them that differ in structure and performance from the parental form because of recombination
of genes. As the children of a brilliant father rarely if ever
attain his exceptional capacities, so too the descendants of
a highbred apple or pear will only rarely equal the parental
species in economic value, size of fruit, or taste. The strong
heterozygosis of fruit varieties makes it practically impossible for offspring raised from seed to repeat the combinations of genes of the parents. However, it cannot be said

that the offspring of our varieties of fruit and potatoes are always inferior or even "degenerate"; from time to time, sometimes seldom, sometimes more often, one finds favorable new combinations among them that match their parents in taste or size of fruit, or that even surpass them (Fig. 55).

Fig. 55. (*Top*) A Cox's Orange Pippin apple; (*below*) fruits from seedlings of the same variety. (After M. Schmidt)

Raising fruit trees from seeds of old cultivated forms has always been an important method of breeding new fruit varieties.

The danger of gradual decline in performance would indeed exist in our cultivated plants if we had breeding varieties that were entirely homozygous in all their decisive genes and hence could not show any segregation in these important characters. Also, in such varieties, owing to the constantly occurring mutations of various kinds, changes in the original genetic constitution would take place that could easily lead to a gradual decline in performance. This also holds true for all varieties of cultivated plants that are the vegetatively produced descendants of a single plant. In theory, all the plants of such a variety should have a completely identical genetic constitution, but this is not the case. Through the constant occurrence of mutations in the body tissue of the plants, hereditary variants appear among the originally homogeneous plant material, which only seldom reaches the value of the original clone. For this reason, a breeder of strawberries, for example, selects from the clones the plants of particularly high yield and takes from them only the slips that he needs for the further propagation of his variety, since only in this way can he maintain its original level of performance.

Thus the "degeneration" of cultivated plants is quite a natural process based partly on heterozygosis and partly on the ability of cultivated plants to mutate. Deterioration in performance becomes manifest as soon as selection by man declines or even ceases. Since wild-plant characters can also appear in cultivated forms, owing to mutation and hybridization, it is possible that cultivated plants, if left to themselves for a long time, "turn wild," that is, revert to wild forms over the course of time.

CHAPTER 4

The History of Plant Breeding,
An Evolutionary Process
Guided by Man

ORIGIN AND AGE OF OUR MOST IMPORTANT
CULTIVATED PLANTS

The origin of cultivated plants is an achievement of plant
breeding, which began at the moment man began methodical
cultivation of wild plants. Thus plant breeding is as old as
agriculture.

As far as we know, this began in the prehistoric civilizations of central Asia, Asia Minor, and Egypt. In central
Asia, agriculture existed as early as the fifth millennium B.C.
In Asia Minor and Egypt, around 4000 B.C. at the latest,
there was a well-developed agriculture that included barley
and emmer as cultivated plants, as well as various legumes
such as peas and vetches. The transition from collecting the
wild forms of these plants to intentionally growing them and
the transformation of the wild species into actual cultivated
plants must date back even further. Emmer, *Triticum dicoccum*, is in all probability derived from the wild form,
T. dicoccoides, which is native to the Middle East. The cultivated barleys are derived from two different wild forms.
Hordeum agriocrithon, a polystichous wild form, is a native
of the Far Eastern gene center, while *H. spontaneum*, a
distichous wild species, is native to the Middle East. Accordingly, in the Far East are found many varieties of polystichous barley, *H. polystichon*, and among them many varieties with naked grains, while the Middle Eastern gene

center is also a center for variety in the distichous cultivated barley, *H. distichon.*

From the centers of the earliest agricultural civilization of the Middle East, agriculture, and with it the first cultivated plants, advanced toward the west and northwest and in a very short time became the common property of all neolithic tribes in Europe. In the course of time, the first cultivated plants were joined over and over again by new species. About 1000 years after the first appearance of emmer we find einkorn, *Triticum monococcum,* as a cultivated plant of the band-pattern-ceramic civilization. It may have originated in the Balkans from the native wild form of einkorn, *T. boeoticum,* by immediate cultivation. In Asia Minor, cultivated einkorn did not make its appearance until some 1000 years later, in the ruins of Troy. Vavilov thinks it possible that the einkorn of Asia Minor may have become a cultivated plant after first having been a weed among emmer. If this assumption is correct, we would have to account for the fact that einkorn became a cultivated plant in two different places and in two rather different ways, so that it should be regarded in one case as a primary, and in the other as a secondary, cultivated plant.

Of the various 42-chromosome spelts, Indian dwarf wheat, *Triticum sphaerococcum,* was to be found during the Neolithic era, and in the height of the Neolithic era common wheat, *T. aestivum,* was added. The first 42-chromosome wheats coming to Europe from their native region in the Middle East were the compact Indian dwarf wheats, which were the predominant spelt varieties everywhere in the earliest days of civilization. First in the Bronze Age, and then in the Iron Age, the loose-eared common wheat, which perhaps had already come to Europe with the Indian dwarf wheat, gained increasing importance. Spelt, *T. spelta,* seems to have originated in central Europe in the late Neolithic era. Its derivation still has not been explained. It is unlikely that it originated in Europe directly from a cross between emmer and *Aegilops squarrosa*, since *Aegilops* does not occur at all in central Europe. It probably evolved in Europe by gene mutation from common wheat or after a cross with emmer. Cultivated emmer is the original form of the hard-grained durum wheat, *T. durum*, and of the other 28-chromosome wheats. The first reliable discoveries of hard-grained wheat in Egypt date back to Greco-Roman times. Poulard, or rivet, wheat, *T. turgidum*, seems to be of even later origin: the first reports are encountered in sixteenth-century herbals. We are even less well informed about the time of origin of the other 28-chromosome wheat species.

Rye, *Secale cereale*, makes its first appearance among the Bronze Age findings at Olmütz in Moravia. Evidently it then dispersed rapidly in the region north of the Alps and became the most important bread grain of the Slavs, Celts, and Teutons. The cultivated oat, *Avena fatua* ssp. *sativa*, is derived from the wild oat, *Avena fatua* ssp. *fatua*, a wild species native to eastern Europe and the Middle East, in which region it became a weed among emmer and barley and arrived in central Europe together with these cultivated plants. In the vicinity of Merseburg, large amounts of gathered weed oats have been discovered in an archaeological site from the Hallstatt Period. When the worsening of climate during the Bronze Age impaired conditions for the cultivation of emmer in this region, the emmer was replaced by oats, which as weeds had acquired the characters of a cultivated plant. In Roman times, oats were an important cultivated plant among the Teutons. According to Thellung, *Avena strigosa* ssp. *strigosa*, as a weed among cultivated oats, developed different characters from its wild original form, *Avena strigosa* ssp. *barbata*, and has been known as a cultivated plant ever since the Bronze Age, but without ever gaining much importance.

Millet, *Panicum miliaceum*, and Italian millet, *Setaria ital-*

ica, are very ancient cultivated plants. The original form of millet is perhaps *Panicum spontaneum,* which grows wild in central Asia. The barn grass *Setaria viridis,* a weed having worldwide distribution, is probably the progenitor of Italian millet. Vavilov considers central Asia to be the center of origin of both species. They were grown as cultivated plants as early as the Neolithic era and dispersed during that time from the region north of the Black Sea into western Switzerland. From the Bronze Age into the late Middle Ages they were also economically important plants in central Europe. They became unimportant only when bread replaced meal. Millet ranked among the five most important cultivated plants in China as early as 2700 B.C. Some species of millet that were formerly used as cultivated plants, such as barnyard millet, *Echinochloa crus-galli,* and crab grass, *Digitaria sanguinale,* have today descended to the level of weeds. In tropical and subtropical agricultures, three other species of millet are important: sorghum, *Andropogon sorghum,* to which broom corn also belongs, and African millet, *Pennisetum spicatum,* both of which are derived polyphyletically from the hybridization of a great number of wild African species; and raggee, *Eleusine coracana,* which probably originated from the weed species *E. indica,* which is widely distributed in the tropics. Presumably all these species are of African origin, but today they are distributed as cultivated plants in the warm zones of the entire world. Sorghum in particular seems to have come rather early by way of India to East Asia, where, known in China as kaoliang, it has gained an important position among cultivated plants. Teff, *Eragrostis abyssinica,* the wild ancestral species of which is believed to be *E. pilosa,* has been confined as a cultivated plant within its country of origin, Ethiopia.

Maize, *Zea mays,* is closely related to millet. We know nothing yet about its wild original forms. The primary center of diversity of cultivated maize is in the Andes of Bolivia and Peru, where it was the most important cultivated plant even in prehistoric times. The original varieties of maize were forms having glumes. From these evolved varieties with naked grains, which are the ones that are grown almost exclusively today. Maize was introduced into Central America from South America. Spontaneous hybridization occurred between the still rather primitive cultivated maize and closely related wild species belonging to the genus *Tripsacum.* On one hand, this hybridization led to the evolution of a great diversity of forms, and, on the other, to a marked improvement in the yield capacity of the maize plant. With the discovery of America, maize, the only cultivated cereal grain of American origin, spread rapidly in Europe and in the whole of the Old World.

The last cereal of worldwide economic significance—rice, *Oryza sativa*—is also an ancient cultivated plant. Together with two species of millet, wheat, and soybeans, it belongs to the five cultivated plants that, according to a decree of the emperor Chen-Nung in 2700 B.C., had to be planted by the emperor himself in a solemn ceremony during the spring celebration. Thus all these cultivated plants are probably more than 4500 years old. *Oryza fatua,* a wild species that is widespread in Southeast Asia, is considered the progenitor of rice. At an early date, rice made its way from China to Korea and Japan, and, by way of Indochina and India, to the Sunda Islands and the Philippines. During the first half of the last millennium B.C., its cultivation spread from India to Persia and from there into the irrigated regions of the Euphrates. Rice was first grown in Europe in Italy in 1468, and it reached America from Madagascar in 1694.

Finally, sugar cane, *Saccharum officinarum,* ranks among the economically important cultivated plants of the grass family. It does not belong to the group of the oldest cultivated plants. In Southeast Asia or the East Indies, it originated from native wild grasses, probably from crosses between *Saccharum spontaneum* and *S. robustum,* and was an esteemed cultivated plant in India around 300 B.C. It reached Egypt about the middle of the seventh century and got to Spain about a hundred years later. From Spain it was introduced into America early in the sixteenth century, where it spread within a hundred years all over Central and South America.

A very ancient cultivated plant—about as old as barley or emmer—is flax, *Linum usitatissimum.* It is most probably derived from the wild form, *Linum hispanicum* (see Fig. 51), which is native to the Mediterranean region and the Middle East. Its transformation into a cultivated plant most probably took place in the Middle Eastern gene center. Primitive decumbent flaxes are still found there that are quite close to the wild form. During the northwest migration of cultivated flax, the tall-stalked and small-seeded fiber flaxes evolved, while in the Mediterranean area the large-seeded, short-stalked linseed-oil flax developed. In India, primitive small-seeded, short-stalked forms are still grown for oil production, while in the Ethiopian gene center flax has become a dwarf food plant whose seeds are ground for flour.

Among the most valuable gifts that mankind has received from the New World is the potato, *Solanum tuberosum.* For tuber-forming species of *Solanum* closely related to the cultivated potato, three different diversity centers are known in South America: one in Mexico, containing many wild species; a second one in the Bolivian and Peruvian Andes, where various species of cultivated potatoes exist; and finally a third one on Chiloé Island and in the coastal mountains of the neighboring continent. Here various wild species are found as well as cultivated potatoes that are quite close to our cultivated European and American breeding varieties and might well be taken as their original forms.

Among the wild forms of the potato we know both non-polyploid species and species of widely differing degrees of polyploidy; these have tubers that are mostly small and of little value. The tubers of some of these species are collected nevertheless, and these species represent the transition to the cultivated potato, in which we also find species with 24, 36, 48, and 60 chromosomes. Most of these cultivated potatoes have remained primitive "Indian" potatoes. Genuine economic importance has been achieved only by the 48-chromosome polyploid species *Solanum tuberosum.* There are various views concerning the original form of the cultivated potato; while some think that the 24-chromosome species *S. vernei* is the progenitor of *S. tuberosum,* others have concluded from cytologic data that *S. stenotomum,* also a 24-chromosome species of the nonpolyploid original species, must be at least very closely related to the cultivated potato.

The cultivated potato, *Solanum tuberosum,* includes two subspecies: *tuberosum* and *andigenum.* The latter is a highly polymorphic cultivated plant. Owing to its strong dependence on day length for tuber development—satisfactory tubers being formed under short-day conditions—it has not been able to gain any great economic importance outside of its native region. The subspecies *tuberosum,* on the other hand, is dependent on day length neither for its development nor for its formation of tubers, in particular. This is why—out of the many tuber-forming species of *Solanum* that played a role in the most ancient civilizations of South America and that were, during the empire of the Incas, the most important food plants at altitudes of 2000 to 4000 meters—only *Solanum tuberosum* ssp. *tuberosum* became the original form of the European and North American potato. From the relatively few forms that were imported into Europe at the end of the sixteenth century and then again in the nineteenth century has evolved the wealth of cultivated potatoes that are grown today. It is only very recently that other cultivated and wild species have begun to play a role in potato breeding as carriers of important genes for resistance to disease, the Colorado beetle, drought, and frost.

The tomato *Lycopersicon esculentum* is an ancient cultivated plant of South America that is presumably derived from *L. pimpinellifolium.* Although it was brought to Europe rather early, it did not gain ground as a food plant before the last century. In marked contrast, the French bean, which is native to the same region, spread over the whole world so rapidly after the discovery of America, as did the tobacco plant, that their New World origin was disputed for some time.

One of the most important cultivated plants of the temperate zone, the sugar beet, *Beta vulgaris* ssp. *esculenta* var. *altissima,* is of very recent origin. Its progenitor was *B. vulgaris* ssp. *perennis* var. *maritima,* which grows along the coasts of the North Sea and the Mediterranean. In the sixth to fourth centuries B.C. in the eastern Mediterranean region, the first cultivated forms developed plants resembling mangel-wurzel whose leaves were used as vegetables. In fact, the ancient Greeks were acquainted with "salad" beets having thickened roots with white or red flesh. In the eighteenth century, the common beet evolved through enlargement of the root of the mangel-wurzel and from "salad" beets. After the discovery of sugar in beets by Markgraf in 1747, Achard began at the start of the nineteenth century to develop the white Silesian beet into an actual "sugar beet." In the course of about a hundred years, breeding succeeded in increasing the sugar content of the beets from 6–7.5 percent to about 20–24 percent (Fig. 57). Here, planned plant breeding performed its first feat: the creation of a completely new, valuable cultivated plant.

Let us now look briefly at the origin and age of some im-

portant vegetable species. The radish *Raphanus sativus* and
the common garden radish are most probably derived from
charlock, *Raphanus raphanistrum*, with which they crossed
fertilely. The radish belongs to the group of the oldest cultivated plants and evidently reached the Mediterranean
region rather early. According to Herodotus, it was sup-
plied as a condiment to the workmen on the pyramid of
Cheops, together with onions and garlic. While the diversity
center of the radish is in the Far East, the common garden
radish, according to Vavilov, is a native of central Asia. It
has been known in Europe only since the sixteenth century.
Like peas, the garden bean, *Vicia faba*, belongs among the
first cultivated plants of mankind. The small-seeded forms,
the so-called field beans, come from the central Asian gene
center, while the large-seeded garden beans have their
diversity center in the area of the Mediterranean. The leek,
Allium porrum, which is native to the Mediterranean region,
was cultivated in antiquity. Discoveries of carrot seeds in
Neolithic deposits make it seem feasible that this plant,
Daucus carota—believed by Thellung to have originated
from a spontaneous cross of our native wild carrot with the
Mediterranean species *D. maximus*—was grown as a cultivated plant quite early. Reliable reports of cultivated forms
of carrots exist from the first century. A plant native to central Europe that has been grown for three or four thousand
years is the parsnip, *Pastinaca sativa*, which used to be a
very important food plant. Since the Middle Ages, however,
it has been displaced more and more by celery, *Apium
graveolens*, which grows wild in all the coastal regions of
Europe, western Asia, and North Africa, and which became
a cultivated plant in the Mediterranean region. Spinach
came from the central Asian gene center, where it may have
originated from *Spinacia tetranda* (Fig. 16). In medieval
times it was brought to Europe by the Arabians. Head let-

tuce, *Lactuca sativa,* most probably is derived from prickly lettuce, *L. scariola,* which is also common in central Europe. The region of origin of the cultivated form seems to be the Middle East or the eastern Mediterranean. It was among the most important vegetable species in ancient Egypt, and was cultivated by the Greeks and Romans in numerous subvarieties that did not form heads. During the time of Charlemagne it reached central Europe. The head-forming lettuce, which is grown predominantly today, was mentioned for the first time by Leonard Fuchs in 1543. *Cucumis sativus* var. *hardwickii,* growing wild in the Himalayas, is considered the progenitor of the cultivated cucumber, *C. sativus* L., which has long been a cultivated plant in India. From there the cucumber went to Egypt in early times and was spread to central Europe by the Romans.

Let us now have a look at our most important fruit varieties. Remnants of apples and pears have been found in Neolithic lake dwellings, perhaps early primitive cultivated forms that originated from the native crab, *Malus communis* ssp. *silvestris,* and from wild pears. Besides the crab, another wild apple, *Malus communis* ssp. *pumila* var. *domestica,* played a role in the origin of the common apple; so, too, did spontaneous hybrids of the two forms, distributed respectively from western or eastern Europe to central Asia, and also the cherry apple, or Siberian crab, *M. baccata,* a native of Asia. Similarly, various subspecies of *Pyrus communis,* as well as other *Pyrus* species, have contributed to the origin of the common pear. The ancient Romans were acquainted with different varieties of these pomes, which probably came to them from the Middle East and Greece. The selection of especially valuable seedlings and, in recent times, methodical breeding have led to the origin of the numerous varieties that we know today.

The cherry *Prunus avium* is derived from wild forms that

are widespread in western Asia and Europe. The polyploid morello cherry, *P. cerasus,* however, is a native of the Middle East. Neither species was apparently taken under cultivation until historical times. Hybridization of the two species has yielded amarelles.

The origin of the plum as an allopolyploid between the cherry plum and the blackthorn has already been mentioned. The region of origin may be the contact zone of the two species in the Middle East, where nonpolyploid-species hybrids can also be found. The plum must have been cultivated quite early, for plum "stones" have been found in Neolithic and Bronze Age remains. The Romans were acquainted with a large number of varieties. In central Europe the cultivation of plums has expanded greatly ever since the sixteenth century.

Numerous varieties of the peach *Prunus persica* were cultivated around 2000 B.C. in China, where wild forms also occurred. At the beginning of the Christian era it had spread west as far as Persia, and in another hundred years or so it was introduced into the Mediterranean region and southern Germany by the Romans.

Wild forms of the apricot possessing small, bad-tasting fruit and bitter stones are found from Asia Minor to Manchuria. The gene center of this species is in the Far East. The cultivated forms emigrated westward simultaneously with the peach, reaching the Mediterranean area about the same time.

A very old cultivated plant is the grape, *Vitis vinifera.* Wild grapes are still found today from central Asia to western Europe. Where and when these wild forms were first taken under cultivation is impossible to tell. It is certain, however, that in Egypt during the time of the first dynasties grapes were cultivated and wine was drunk and that there were already some distinct varieties of grapes.

Berries, on the other hand, are very recent cultivated plants. Although raspberries and blackberries are old gathered fruits, they were not cultivated before the Middle Ages. Similar conditions hold for gooseberries and currants, which are also natives of central Europe. They were only rarely mentioned in the sixteenth century as cultivated plants, and only five varieties of gooseberries were known at the middle of the eighteenth century. Cultivation of these species spread from Belgium and northern France. Strawberries are also among those species that have only recently been cultivated forms. The 14-chromosome common wild strawberry, *Fragaria vesca,* was grown in French gardens in the fourteenth century; in the sixteenth century, it was occasionally joined by the 14-chromosome alpine strawberry, *Fragaria viridis.* Varieties were bred in the seventeenth century from the Hautbois strawberry, *F. moschata,* that have disappeared since then. Of decisive importance for the development of the strawberry into an economically important cultivated plant, however, was the introduction of the 56-chromosome scarlet Virginian strawberry, *F. virginiana,* at the beginning of the seventeenth century, and the 56-chromosome large-fruited Chilean strawberry, *F. chiloensis,* and the spontaneous hybridization of these species in Holland in the middle of the eighteenth century, which led to the origin of the first large-fruited pineapple strawberry, *F. grandiflora.*

Except for alfalfa, *Medicago sativa,* which was grown early by the Persians from the Middle East to the Mediterranean region, and also from 470 B.C. by the Greeks as valuable food for horses, green fodder legumes were not taken under cultivation until more recent times. Sainfoin, *Onobrychis sativa,* has been raised since the fifteenth century; red clover, *Trifolium pratense,* bird's-foot clover, *Lotus corniculatus,* and yellow alfalfa, *Medicago falcata,* since the seventeenth century; alsike clover, *Trifolium hybridum,* since the eighteenth. In the nineteenth century, crimson clover, *Trifolium incarnatum,* and vetch-leaved sainfoin, *Onobrychis viciifolia,* were added. Dutch clover, *Trifolium repens,* white melilot, *Melilotus albus,* and common melilot, *M. officinalis,* plus the economically important grasses have only recently been taken under cultivation and been improved through breeding. Forest plants are still cultivated wild plants. Breeding of forest plants was begun only a short time ago.

The modest segment of the history of cultivated plants that we have been able to give here shows that the most important of man's food plants, the cereals, belong for the most part among the oldest cultivated plants, being at least 6000 years old. New species have been added over and over again to these first cultivated plants, and thus the group of cultivated plants has grown continuously over the course of time. The increase in the number of cultivated plants is due, on one hand, to man's having always taken wild plants under cultivation, and on the other to the fact that the number of cultivated plants in individual countries and civilizations has enlarged considerably through the exchange of different cultivated plants between individual gene centers and between entire continents.

However, it is not true that the number of cultivated plants has always just increased for 6000 years. In some instances, plants that once played a role as cultivated plants have been displaced by a species capable of better performance and finally have disappeared altogether from the ranks of our cultivated plants. Various such cases have already been mentioned. Species that formerly grew in central Europe but are no longer known today as cultivated plants are skirret, *Sium sisarum;* rampion, *Campanula rapunculus;* alexanders, *Smyrnium olusaturum;* the cultivated form of caraway, with fleshy, edible roots; nightshade, *Solanum nigrum, S. humile,* and *S. villosum;* rocket, *Eruca sativa;* and

soapwort, *Saponaria officinalis.* Dye-producing plants, such
as madder, *Rubia tinctorum,* woad, *Isatis tinctoria,* dyer's
weed, *Reseda luteola,* common saw-wort, *Serratula tinctoria,*
and safflower, *Carthamus tinctorius,* were first displaced
from the ranks of cultivated plants by cheaper and more
effective tropical plants such as indigo, and then eventually
by synthetic dyes.

Thus even among cultivated plants rivalry exists to a certain degree. More efficient breeding varieties displace primitive forms (Fig. 56), and species showing little evolutionary
potential are replaced by new cultivated plants with wider
genetic latitude of variation that can be bred faster for
higher yields and better quality. As in the struggle for
existence in nature, so too among cultivated plants the
better plant displaces the less good one and eventually re-
places it. Since man's intent is the decisive selective factor
in cultivated plants, selection leads to an increasing improvement in the utility of plants for man, that is, to a

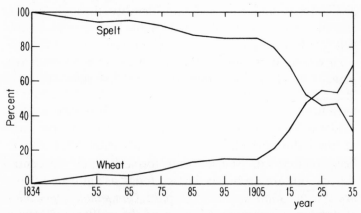

Fig. 56. The more valuable cultivated plant takes the place of less efficient forms: displacement of spelt by common wheat in Württemberg,
1834–1935. (After K. and F. Bertsch)

constant intensification of cultivated-plant characters. This selective process leading to the origin and perfection of the characters of cultivated plants is called plant breeding.

THE STAGES OF DEVELOPMENT OF PLANT BREEDING

The origin of cultivated plants is only the first step in the comprehensive evolutionary process that we call plant breeding. To go deeply into the subject would take a separate volume, but it does seem appropriate to give at the end of this book a brief outline of the history of plant breeding.

The "age of wild plants," when man was confined to collecting edible parts of wild-growing plants, ended when he started intentionally to grow wild plants. With the cultivation of plants by man, the transformation of the wild form into the cultivated plant began. It proceeded partly by conscious selection and propagation of mutants that occurred and were found at random and of new combinations, and partly unconsciously through the selective action of agriculture, as we have seen it in the origin of cultivated-plant characters in weeds. The importance of large-fruitedness and large-seededness for the successful selection of more efficient plants was realized quite early—the Romans recommended using the largest grain for sowing in order to obtain particularly efficient plants. Apart from this, efforts to obtain hereditary improvement in cultivated plants were rather slight and hence not very effective. It is understandable that the origin and development of cultivated plants took a long time, under the circumstances, and led only to relatively insignificant improvement in their performance. The result of this period of plant breeding is the origin of "field varieties," unpretentious varieties with relatively low yields and frequently of minor quality but excellently adapted to the climate of their region of origin.

The evolution of cultivated plants did not reach a new stage until the nineteenth century. The increasing population density of central and western Europe made higher yield among cultivated agricultural plants imperative. Thus the breeding of varieties having higher yields than those of the older field varieties became important, and, since higher prices were involved, it was also economically rewarding. During the nineteenth century, an increasing number of private breeding stations came into being that successfully tried to breed more efficient varieties from primitive field varieties in our most important species of cultivated plants.

The plant breeding of the nineteenth century, however, had not only an economic but also a scientific basis. The works of Darwin show the importance of selection for the origin of cultivated plants and domestic animals as well as for the origin of species in nature. Theoretical research led rapidly to efforts to examine their effectiveness for practical agricultural purposes, and thus plant breeding in this period was marked by the application of purposeful and conscious selection. Selective breeding was simplified and promoted by investigation of the mineral metabolism of plants by Liebig, which led to the development of inorganic fertilizers and consequently to a considerable improvement in the nutrient supply for growing soils. This in turn made it possible to select the most efficient forms from among dissimilar mixtures of genetically very diverse forms, which field varieties are, and to obtain from among them breeding varieties capable of reacting to an ample supply of inorganic nutrients with increased production of organic substances, that is, varieties with higher yields. Although precise knowledge of the laws of heredity was lacking, the plant breeding of this period developed methods that permitted examination of the offspring of individual plants that seemed especially valuable and made it possible to decide whether the performance of the special plants concerned was genetically determined or merely the result of particularly favorable random environmental conditions. The results obtained in this fashion were assured by further investigations in so-called experimental "breeding gardens," so that eventually only top-quality varieties came to the market from the breeders. The demand of the times for higher yield and the private economic interests of breeders had the effect that this "period of selective breeding" led mainly to an increase in yield, often at the expense of quality.

The economic achievements in plant breeding in this period were extraordinary for those plants that were intensively worked on by breeders. The most brilliant performance of selective breeding was the creation of a completely new cultivated plant, the sugar beet, by the intentional increase of sugar content in the root of the plant (Fig. 57). Further success has been achieved in the breeding of pota-

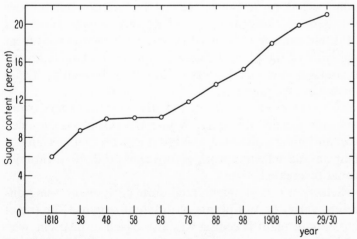

Fig. 57. Increase of sugar content in the sugar beet through selective breeding. (After G. Becker)

toes and cereals, and if the rye variety of Petkus today occupies nearly 50 percent of the total rye acreage of the world it is because of planned selective breeding.

In this period, when breeding was dominated by selection, it was possible for the selection of one valuable individual plant to create a top-quality breeding variety, giving, under special circumstances, a new and unexpected inducement to breeding in general. The classic example is the origin of the well-known Squarehead wheat. In the 1860's, a British farmer named Taylor found a single plant in a field of Victoria wheat that attracted his attention by its short, compact growth, strong straw, and short and compact ears. He harvested it, cultivated the grains separately, and found that the offspring were exactly like the mother plant. The offspring were bred selectively for a number of years following, and by 1871 a variety had developed from the "foundling" plant that surpassed all other varieties in yield.

We know of other such "foundling varieties" from this same period; for instance, one day the East German breeder Dr. Bensing noticed a particularly fine panicle in an oat field. He collected it, sowed it, and was able to breed from the grain of the plant, which was apparently largely homozygous, a new oat variety, "Bensing's Foundling Oat," merely by propagation.

However, even in this period, the plant breeders' work was not usually this easy. With most plants—sugar beet, rye, and other cultivated plants—it usually took decades of painstaking selective work before new productive varieties could be created.

Selection was supplemented quite early by crossing different varieties and plants of different origins. The use of crossing in plant breeding was also based on Darwin, who had seen it as an essential means for producing a great diversity of forms. Thus, crosses at first were made only in order to amplify the material for selection. Soon, however, combining properties of different varieties by means of crossing was begun. Hybridization even between different species and genera was performed; the well-known Rimpau wheat-rye hybrid was a product of hybridizing genera at that time. With no knowledge of the laws of heredity, and solely by means of careful observation and rigid selection, it was possible to achieve a significant increase in yield among cereals by means of hybridization. A specially out-standing example of crossbreeding at this time was the breeding of club wheat, which originated from a cross be-tween low-yield, long- and loose-eared field wheat and the high-yield English Squarehead wheat. The short, rigid stalks inherited from the Squarehead wheat gave the new variety a greater rigidity. This proved particularly valuable after increased fertilization, when the old long-culmed varieties tended to bend and lie down. Thus new wheat varieties had been created through crossing that could bear increased fertilization without damage. The new "intensive" varieties are based on just such varieties; they are capable of re-sponding to heavy fertilization with high yields. Crossing also played a role in the nineteenth century in the breeding of potatoes and cereals.

The "rediscovery" of Mendel's laws of heredity around the turn of the century and the methodical application of them in plant breeding—for which special mention goes to Erich von Tschermack, one of the three discoverers of these rules—introduced a new chapter of plant breeding that we may best call the "period of plant breeding determined by genetics." This period is characterized above all by the practical application of the knowledge gained from the laws of heredity in plant breeding. Thus plant breeding had scientific foundation, and success no longer depended pri-marily on chance and the fortuitous hand of the breeder;

now he could plan his work properly, basing it on the known laws of heredity, and predict the prospects for certain desired breeding results with some certainty. For one thing, combination breeding was based on the principles of Mendelian genetics, which, from the knowledge of Mendel's law of independent assortment of genes, methodically undertook by crossbreeding to combine in one variety favorable characters existing in different varieties. The well-known Swedish scientist Nilsson-Ehle had the first success in this field of plant breeding. He succeeded in combining, by means of crossbreeding, the winter resistance of the Swedish field wheat with the high yield capacity of the English Squarehead wheat, thus raising the yield of the Swedish winter wheat varieties about 25 percent (Fig. 58).

The successful work of Nilsson-Ehle stimulated a large number of similar breeding experiments. By breeding early-ripening spring grains the cultivation of spring wheat could be expanded farther north in Europe and America; resistance to pests, drought, and frost, and rigidity, could be and have been crossbred into valuable breeding varieties.

At first, hybrid breeding was based on purely theoretical knowledge about the "luxuriant growth of hybrids," which, in the case of maize, led to such great economic successes that in the United States today practically nothing but hybrid varieties are grown.

We have become acquainted above with the importance of various kinds of mutations for the origin of cultivated-plant characters. They have the same importance for the improvement of these influential characters. Nowadays, through investigations of the mutation-causing effects of X-rays, radioactive substances, and chemicals, we have the ability to exploit the findings in plant breeding, which is thus entering a new era that will be characterized by the "breeding of mutations." With various methods of inducing mutations experimentally, totally new ways to create a great wealth of forms are at hand, which will be of the highest importance for the further evolution of our cultivated plants. We are still on the edge of this new epoch in plant breeding. The successes that have been achieved through muta-

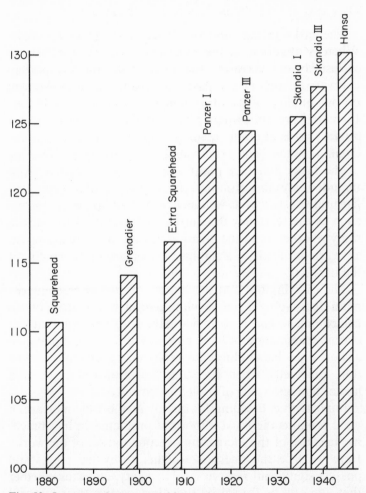

Fig. 58. Increase of average yields of winter wheat in Sweden through breeding. (After H. Brücher)

tion breeding during this short time, however, warrant the expectation that we shall be able to improve our cultivated plants to a considerable degree.

AIMS AND ACCOMPLISHMENTS OF PLANT BREEDING

The tasks facing modern plant breeding are manifold. Whereas attention in the nineteenth century was focused exclusively on increasing the yield of the most important cultivated plants, in the past few decades the improvement of the quality of plant products has come to the fore. Increased protein content and ease of baking have become primary goals of grain breeding. Improved taste, tenderness, vitamin content, and preservability and storability are some of the tasks that face plant and vegetable breeders. Also included are the elimination of disagreeable-tasting or harmful substances as well as of other wild-plant characters such as the tendency of cherries and tomatoes to crack in rainy weather. And the creation of pest- and disease-resistant varieties leads to a significant increase in the quality of the harvest.

The carrying out and the success of quality breeding depend decisively on the development of mechanical, physical, chemical, and mycologic methods of research that will permit examination of large numbers of individual plants in a short time. Paper chromatography may also play a crucial role, especially when breeding for improved taste or a higher biologic value of protein is involved.

Important as breeding for quality may be, the increase of yield remains the most important problem of plant breeding because of the increasing overpopulation of the world. Here we face the question whether cultivated plants still possess significant reserve yield capacity, and thus whether they can still be forced by breeding to raise their material production greatly.

First, we must pause here briefly to consider how much the yield capacity of plants has already been improved. We cannot make any statement about the differences that exist between the yield of wild forms and that of the "field varieties" evolved from them, but they may well be considerable. The increase in productivity achieved through selective breeding has been estimated to be between 50 and 100 percent of the performance of the original "field variety." Although hybrid breeding has been used in the majority of breeding stations only since World War I, the yields so far have been improved by 12 to 25 percent. The cultivation of hybrid varieties of maize, which show a yield of 20 to 37 percent over that of single varieties, nowadays gives the United States an annual crop of 15 to 20 million more tons than before; transferring this method of breeding to another economically important plant, the sugar beet, increased this plant's yield 9 to 11 percent. The first successes of mutation breeding have already been pointed out. These new methods of plant breeding are, for the most part, still in the early stages of application; more decisive results will have to await the future. In addition, many cultivated plants that have been neglected by breeders can still be greatly improved today by simple breeding methods. A number of varieties of German flax that came on the market between the two world wars owe their origin to simple selection from "field varieties." Until recently, hemp was essentially a cultivated wild plant; through the development of a suitable method of selection, the fiber content has been increased about 100 percent, and in some breeds even as much as 200 percent. Many other cultivated plants provide similar favorable breeding prospects, for instance, plants that have been neglected by private breeders because breeding is relatively unprofitable, such as grasses and forage plants, many varieties of fruit, and forest plants. Even with such a popular cultivated plant as the pineapple strawberry, R. v.

Sengbusch was able, through hybridization and selection, to develop new breeds that surpassed well-known older varieties by 100 to 200 percent, and it seems that the limits of performance still have not been reached. Worldwide crop losses through plant disease and pests in grain and potatoes, even if they are figured at only 20 percent of the possible yield, amount to 118 million tons of grain and 40 million tons of potatoes annually, which is enough to feed nearly 500 million people. If losses among other cultivated plants are added to these, it is evident that breeding for resistance alone could contribute significantly to abolishing famine in the world.

It is still possible nowadays to create high-yield cultivated plants from wild plants. Examples are provided by the kok-saghyz, or Russian dandelion, *Taraxacum kok-saghyz,* which for two decades has been raised and improved by breeding in Russia and Canada, and by the creation of cultivated forms of blueberries in North America.

Numerous species of microorganisms, bacteria, fungi, and algae are being grown methodically on a large scale, improved through breeding, and slowly developed into new cultivated plants. This is the case and has been for some time with races of yeast that are used in the brewing industry. Today, numerous other microorganisms have been added to these yeast fungi that we can use to produce food, forage, and important organic substances. Thus today citric acid is produced by means of the well-known mold *Aspergillus niger;* particularly productive breeds that have been obtained partly by induced mutation are used for this process. A mutant of the very closely related species *A. terreus* is used in the production of the technologically important itaconic acids, which can be used for stabilizing fatty oils and as raw material in the production of plexiglas, unbreakable glass, imitation jewelry, stiff and flexible plastics, cleansing agents, and other economically important products. Another cultivated fungus plant of this group may now be included, which often used to cause severe poisoning, *Claviceps purpurea,* the producer of formations in rye known as ergot. Through selective breeding of this fungus, the alkaloid content of ergot that is used in gynecology has been raised from 0.02 to 0.5 percent. Above all, through breeding efficient varieties of bacteria and fungi, the production of antibiotics by a number of these microorganisms has been increased to such a degree that the price of medicines derived from them could be very substantially reduced, thus making it possible to use antibiotics not only to fight disease in men and animals, but also to prevent and eliminate plant disease and to be used as growth-promoting fodder. Several species of fungi are used in the production of "mycellium proteins" from sulfide wastes of the cellulose industry, while other fungi and bacteria are used in the production of various vitamins. It has been pointed out again and again recently that unicellular green algae can produce much more organic substance than the most efficient higher plants can. Whereas the sugar beet, the cultivated plant having the highest yield, annually produces organic substance amounting approximately to 3500 calories per square meter, the mass cultivation of algae during the same length of time yielded 30,000 calories, according to results obtained by the Carbohydrate Biological Research Station in Essen, Germany; Harder and von Witsch estimate possible production under optimum conditions at 144,000 calories per square meter per year. The culture of algae is looked upon now as a method that may at some future date make it possible to provide additional food for starving mankind. Here too, as soon as the mass cultivation of algae has passed the experimental stage, breeding will be set up in order to create varieties of algae that are particularly suitable for cultivation.

From these few examples, we can see that plant breeding

still faces tasks of various kinds, and that it still has the potential for considerable improvement in cultivated plants and thus can continue to contribute its share to adjusting man's food margin to the population increase, at least for some time. How well or how poorly it can fulfill this task will depend very much on the development of basic research, since the progress of theoretical knowledge ultimately determines the success of applied science. The possibilities and means available to theoretical biology today and tomorrow can thus decide whether our grandchildren and great-grandchildren will still have enough food, or whether, within a relatively short time, famine may become a permanent condition with us.

LITERATURE*

Anderson, E., *Plants, Man and Life* (London, 1954).

Bertsch, K. and F., *Geschichte unserer Kulturpflanzen* (Stuttgart, 1947).

Brücher, H., *Stammesgeschichte der Getreide* (Stuttgart, 1950).

De Candolle, A., *Origin of Cultivated Plants* (reprint of the second edition, 1886; Hafner, New York, 1959).

Crane, M. B., and W. J. C. Lawrence, *The Genetics of Garden Plants* (London, 1952).

Darwin, C., *The Variation of Animals and Plants under Domestication* (New York, 1868).

Kappert, H., *Die vererbungswissenschaftlichen Grundlagen der Züchtung* (Berlin, Hamburg, 1953).

Kuckuck, H., *Von der Wildpflanze zur Kulturpflanze* (Berlin, 1934).

Roemer, T., A. Scheibe, J. Schmidt, and E. Woermann, *Handbuch der Landwirtschaft,* vol. 2, Pflanzenbau (Berlin, Hamburg, 1953).

Scheibe, A., *Einführung in die allgemeine Pflanzenzüchtung* (Stuttgart, 1951).

Schiemann, E., *Entstehung der Kulturpflanzen* (Handbuch der Vererbungswissenschaft, III, L; Berlin, 1932).

——"Entstehung der Kulturpflanzen," *Ergeb. Biol.* (Berlin, 1943), 409.

——*Weizen, Roggen, Gerste* (Jena, 1948).

Schwanitz, F., "Die Entstehung der Nutzpflanzen als Modell fur die Evolution der gesamten Pflanzenwelt," *Die Evolution der Organismen* (ed. 2, Stuttgart, 1955), p. 713.

Sengbusch, R. von, *Pflanzenzüchtung und Rohstoffversorgung* (Leipzig, 1937).

Thellung, A., "Kulturpflanzeneigenschaft bei Unkräutern," *Veröffentl. Geobotan. Inst. Rübel in Zürich, 3* (1925), 745.

—— "Die Entstehung der Kulturpflanzen," *Naturw. Landwirtsch. 16* (1930).

*For extensive recent references, largely in English, on some of the subjects treated in this book see J. Hutchinson, *Essays on Crop Plant Evolution* (University Press, Cambridge, England, 1965); J. L. Brewbaker, *Agricultural Genetics* (Prentice Hall, New York, 1964).

Vavilov, N. J., *The Origin, Variation, Immunity, and Breeding of Cultivated Plants* (Waltham, Mass., 1951).

Werth, E., *Grabstock, Hacke und Pflug* (Stuttgart, 1955).

Zade, A., *Werdegang und Züchtungsgrundlagen der landwirtschaftlichen Kulturpflanzen* (Leipzig, Berlin, 1921)

INDEX

Alfalfa: crossbreeding, 87–88; origin and age, 154

Algae: culture, to provide food, 167, for development into new plants, 166; future breeding, 7–9

Alleles, 65

Allometric growth of plant organs, 30–32

Allopolyploidy: defined, 96; heterosis in, 107–108; importance in plant breeding, 113–114, disadvantage, 114; role in origin of species, 97–99; in wheat, 99–101

Aneuploidy, 114–115

Anthropochorous plants, 121–122

Autopolyploidy, 96

Avery, A. G., 110

Bacteria, cultured for development of new plants, 166, for other purposes, 167

"Beefsteak" tomatoes, 22

Bensing's foundling oat, 160

Biennialism, advantages, 46–47

Bitterness and toxicity. *See* Toxicity

Blakeslee, H. F., 110

Bud mutations, 79, 80–83

Bursting of carnations from flower doubling, 136, 137

Cabbage, diverse forms, 53–55, origin in gene mutation, 75–78

Cells: enlarged by polyploidy, 17, 18, 27; in gigantism, 16–17, 24, 26–28

Chromosomes: in gigantism, 17–20, 26, 27, 28; mutations, 94–97; *see also* Polyploidy

Colchicine, polyploid induction by, 110

Coloration: from crossbreeding, 92–93; somatic mutation, 79, 80

Correns, C., 5

Crossbreeding, 86–94, 161–162; alfalfa, 87–88; combination of favorable characters, 88–89; combined with gene mutation, 87; garden plants, 92–93; maize, 91–92; new characters produced, 89–90; related genera, hybridization, 92; scarlet-runner bean, 91

Cultigens. *See* Cultivated plants

Cultivated plants: "degeneration," 135–141; derivation from wild species, 2–6 (*see also* Plant breeding); human importance and value, 1–2; native habitats, 128–135 (*see also* Environment; Gene centers); origin and habitats, 5; polyploid, 97–99; primary and secondary, 121–122; relation to animals, 2; worldwide distribution, 128

Darlington, C. D., 19

Darwin, C., 3, 5, 56, 117, 160

De Candolle, A. L. P. P., 2, 3, 5

De Vries, H., 5

Delayed germination and ripening, eliminated in cultivated plants, 43–44

Diseases, desirable properties caused by, 137–139

Dissemination mechanisms: eliminated in cultivated plants, 34, 38; lowered survival power from loss of, 117–118; retained in certain plants, 59–60; in wild plants, 32–34

Environment: influence, 116–142; adaptation to, 119, 123–128; anthropochorous plants, 121–122; cause of rigorous selection, 119; compared with genetic effect, 160; "degeneration" of cultivated plants, 135–141, desirable properties from diseases, 137–139, heterozygosis, 140, 142, misbreeding, 136, stabilized selec-